WHAT MAN MAY BE

WHAT MAN MAY BE

The Human Side of Science

GEORGE RUSSELL HARRISON

"For it is not yet known what man may be."

"All things by immortal power, near or far,
Hiddenly to each other linked are.
That thou canst not stir a flower
Without troubling of a star."

Francis Thompson

WILLIAM MORROW AND COMPANY

New York   *1956*

Four chapters of this book have appeared as
articles in *The Atlantic*.

*Published simultaneously in the Dominion of Canada
by George J. McLeod Limited, Toronto.*

Printed in the United States of America.

Library of Congress Catalog Card Number: 56-8014

To
N. K. H.

Contents

WHAT MAN MAY BE

Chapter One

Science and the Whole Man

This is the day of the ascendancy of science. In the past fifty years scientific knowledge and methods have changed our manner of living more rapidly than any form of human endeavor has ever changed it in the past. In each decade now we get more new understanding of the processes of nature, and more ability to control them, than became available in any previous century. Science is coming to determine how much men can eat, how comfortable they are, how hard they must work, and even how long they will live. Many people view with grave distrust this dependence on what seems to them a materialistic and perhaps directionless effort, and feel that scientists should be curbed in their endeavors to let loose little-understood forces—forces that immerse society in problems which may prove insoluble.

Much misunderstanding arises because most of us, through our newspapers and magazines, make contact with science mainly through its slums, the half-world of such things as flying saucers and water dowsing. We may be set to worrying about technological unemployment, for where will the workman find a job when all the factories are operated by machines under the surveillance of foremen servomechanisms, directed by robot superintendents? Or we may fear that increasing freedom from discomfort, and the new availability of baubles in an age of neon and chromium, may lead man away from the path of spiritual advancement, so that he becomes a jaded seeker after material pleasures. Or we may feel with some poets and mystics that science makes being alive not only less enjoyable, but more dangerous, in giving man new powers without at the same time helping him to choose more surely between good and evil.

Such fears arise from a limited understanding of what science is, and what it can accomplish. Together with art and religion, science is one of the great paths man has cleared in his quest for truth. Art, science, and religion each has its own contribution to make, each its own limitations when packaged in human thought and feeling. Where there is overlapping, contradiction sometimes appears, but there need not be conflict without ultimate resolution. Mystic, musician, man of science, all are limited in their wisdom to the extent that each does not use, in proper degree, all the avenues available for seeking truth. Much is to be gained through increased awareness by each of what is being done by the others.

Being able to understand what scientists do, and how science affects humanity, is mainly a matter of interest. Every lover of mankind owes it to himself to be reasonably well informed about the methods and results of science. In fact, today no one is justified in calling himself a person of culture without some familiarity with scientific matters. It is especially dangerous in these times for statesmen to be ignorant of science. Many who tinker today with the complex operations of society, men who would not dare take a watch or even a lawn mower apart, do not hesitate to remove gears and governors from the intricate mechanisms of a complex modern state.

Martin Luther was once given a watch. It was the latest 1527 model, larger than a present-day alarm clock, and with but a single hand that marked the hours. He became so excited over his new portable time-dissecting device that he decided to study mathematics, so that he could understand how his watch operated. This showed a fine inquiring spirit on the part of a man whose main interests lay in other directions. His modern counterparts owe it to themselves to understand as well as possible how the ticking of atoms can now be measured in billionths of a second, and even what governs the behavior of a positron. It is still more important that they learn how these things affect the spiritual nature of man.

The manner in which scientific facts often turn out to be quite contrary to "common-sense" impressions is illustrated by the prevalent feeling regarding yesterday's "technological unemployment," and today's "automation" of factories. It is natural for laborers to fear the machine, yet successful machines produce many more jobs than they destroy. Early in the century a hundred thousand people who worked in livery stables in the United States lost their jobs as a result of the automobile. Yet from the needs of this machine more than three million new and better jobs soon appeared. Employment opportunities are now increasing fastest in those countries in which technological development is most rapid. In fact, over the past fifty years the number of jobs in America has grown far more rapidly than the population, because of the great number of additional jobs created by machines.

Machines are merely amplifiers of the abilities of workmen, and exist only as they can do man's bidding effectively. It is technology, springing from science, that has enabled society to afford such "luxuries" as lowering the work week from seventy to forty hours with greater take-home pay, and forbidding children to work long hours in sweatshops at degrading tasks. Far from being a slave of the machine, man now has a choice as to whether he will use machines, or remain as he was before, a slave to his poverty and hunger.

Any scientist who feels hurt that the era of material plenty he has helped to usher in is sneeringly called by some cynics "this age of DDT and nylons," can derive comfort from the fact that those who sneer nevertheless buy nylons for their wives and DDT for their mosquitoes. Like philosophers who long for "the good old days," they are also likely to come in at 2:00 A.M. to borrow the scientist's telephone when a child comes down with polio. But it is not enough to say that anyone who objects to the wonders of science can refuse to accept them. In *Pygmalion*, Shaw has Mrs. Higgins say to Mr. Doolittle, when he worries about the effect of new wealth on his character, "You need not suffer all this if you are really in earnest. Nobody can force you to accept this bequest. You can repudiate it." But even the humanists who sincerely believe that the only proper studies for man are languages, arts, and philosophy, know that they cannot resist the blandishments of science, and say like Mr. Doolittle, "That's the tragedy of it, ma'am. It's easy to say chuck it, but I haven't the nerve. We're all intimidated."

One of the greatest obligations of scientists today is to observe the effects of science on other fields of human affairs. We shall in this book explore its impact on the entire man, in helping to produce the balanced man. Besides discussing what man is, and the influence played on him by his environment, we must also consider the effect on him of the new ability science brings to change this environment as he learns better to control matter and energy. Then we must consider the increasing sensitivity to experience that results from the sharpening of man's senses by the instruments science provides, the effect on his emotional nature of his new security and assurance, and the improved ability to prophesy and control the future that results. Our concern must be not only with whether science adds to man's comfort and safety, to his health, security, and enjoyment of life, but whether it adds to his dignity and stature as an individual. We must examine the impact of the methods of science on his thought processes, and finally the integrated effect of all this on his spiritual nature. These form a unified and inspiring picture as we see man revealed, by science as by religion and art, to have capabilities limited only by his own efforts.

2

The demonstration by science of the unity of nature profoundly affects us all. When a spectroscope dissects light from any distant galaxy it reveals only the chemical elements that we find on earth. In this confirmation of a universe, as contrasted with millions of unrelated stars, the scientist shares with the mystic an awareness of that Oneness from which springs our most fundamental feeling of security.

To appreciate the implications of this unity, one needs to understand how even the most complex and diverse things that we can sense are built up as different manifestations of a few simple, basic elements. Physicists have isolated only three kinds of forces in the universe: electric, magnetic, and gravitational, and every push or pull that we can feel seems to be a combination of these. Some scientists hope, by means of unified field theories, to prove that these three forces are merely manifestations of a single elementary force, of which matter is another expression. We know, in any case, that matter is interconvertible with energy, and that the atoms of matter are themselves composed of three basic particles: protons, neutrons, and electrons, plus some additional temporary varieties with which we need not here be concerned.

Now imagine a universe filled with particles of these three kinds flying hither and yon, exerting on each other the three

basic forces, without direction or inter-relation. This indeed
is chaos. Of what use is such a universe?

To build the universe as we know it, a directive force is
needed, which may come from without, or may even be built
into the very nature of the particles themselves. Now we
see pairing of electrons and protons, so that hydrogen atoms
are formed. These in turn join in pairs to produce hydrogen
molecules, which collect as clouds of hydrogen in space,
forming great nebulas. Other protons join with neutrons in
more complex groupings to form the nuclei of new varieties
of atoms, which soon attract to their orbits their respective
quotas of electrons. Eventually we see atoms of nearly a
hundred sorts built up, and we have the basic chemical elements. The degrees to which the forces in the various groupings of particles approach perfect balance differ, so that some
atoms, still unsatisfied, tend to join together as molecules,
while others move about in space alone. Different residual
forces, again, extend from the various molecules. Some types
hold firmly together and form solid matter, like wood or butter. Others cling loosely and form liquids like water. Still
others attract each other so little that they bounce apart when
they collide, and remain as gases like helium and oxygen.
Thus, by a tendency to order which we may call "co-operation," nearly a hundred kinds of atoms have been formed
from the three fundamental particles. These atoms in turn
combine into hundreds of thousands of kinds of molecules,
which further associate to form the millions of objects of our
material world.

Thus on the unity of the first picture is superposed the
concept of order. The universe now is no longer chaotic;
each particle moves, not alone, but under the combined and
ordered influence of its fellows. From three kinds of basic
particles with limited individual capacities have been produced millions of new entities forming a physical world.

About all that a million electrons can do if left to their own devices is to exert a repulsive force on each other, and so in varying degrees with protons and neutrons. But let them arrange themselves properly in atoms, and these in molecules, and mold and combine these molecules in turn, and you can make a spark plug that will help carry a plane and men across the Atlantic. By arranging selected atoms in still more complex ways nature can produce a bee, and then even a swarm of bees. These bees find that if they will co-operate in a hive, instead of living each to himself, they can keep warmer in winter, and so can gather nectar and spread pollen several weeks earlier in spring than a hermit insect dare show his face.

So we find diversity arising from unity, and complexity from simplicity, through the exercise of a co-operative directing force. Men call this force by different names, but this need not concern us here, for we are now discussing only phenomena that science has revealed.

Physicists have discovered a great rule of nature which they call the Second Law of Thermodynamics. This tells man how to measure his flight from chaos. Boiled down, it says that if you want to do anything especially remarkable in a physical system you must supply some direction. Molecules left to themselves become chaotic in their motions. A house or a turnip or a man left without orderly control tends to decay; to produce any one of these objects requires directed effort. Everything we call alive seems to contain such a directing force. A dead seed rots, but a single living seed contains enough directive power to populate a whole planet, given a few billion years, not only with carrots, but with men.

This all sounds rather theoretical, and it is easy to believe that scientists have really been able to accomplish little in understanding what life is and how to produce and control living things. But the door is being opened, and each day brings new insight. For example, in recent years a type of molecule has been found, a plant hormone called auxin, which can cause leaves either to drop off plants or to grow larger. Spraying with selected molecules can make fruit cling more tightly to the branch, or start, speed up, or slow down flowering, or make plant stems longer or shorter, or induce the growing of roots, or kill one type of plant and not another. Chemical foremen molecules growing in a plant, like servo-mechanisms in a factory, regulate the interactions of its various parts, so that it can function as a unified head of lettuce instead of a rotting pool of independent molecules.

A living plant is a factory for storing the energy of sunlight by building such complex molecules as starch, cellulose, and sugar from simple molecules of water and carbon dioxide. Eventually we should be able to regulate such factories as handily as we now control a factory for making tractors. Auxin, which turns out to be the molecule indole-acetic acid, is a superintendent that directs the activities of many foremen molecules in a growing plant. Some of these, merely special arrangements of carbon, oxygen, and other simple atoms, are found to act as they do because they fasten on to certain other molecules through two coupling links instead of one, and thus can act as keys that fit only certain types of molecular locks.

Chemists have separated out and studied several hundred thousand different kinds of molecules that exist in nature, and in addition have fabricated more than twice as many brand-new kinds from the eighty-eight sorts of atoms that nature provides unaided. Many of these new molecules enable us to do things that could not be done before, and it seems probable that eventually useful new jobs will be found for a large proportion of them, from Freon through Dacron to far beyond sulfathiazole.

Science is accused of making living more complex, but,

as we shall see, this is the whole direction of evolution. It also helps *us* to become more complex, which increases our capacity to enjoy living, though it does not guarantee us this enjoyment. As we learn to make contact with nature on an increasing number of levels, our aliveness is intensified and enhanced. The result of existence, whether this be its purpose or not, seems to be to develop creatures that are ever more alive, opening more and improved channels of contact with the universe outside themselves.

3

The universe is not only orderly, it is dynamic. Everywhere about us is ceaseless change. We think of the mountain of granite as an everlasting mass of inert material, but its atoms vibrate and some occasionally explode, and its days are numbered, though in the trillions. Man is being required to learn to cope with events that may happen a million times faster than the flash of a firefly, or a million times more slowly than the recession of a glacier.

Much resentment against science arises from the basic fear of change, which science is likely to accelerate, and the yearning for a return to simplicity. This is usually expressed as annoyance at the bustle of modern living, symbolized by the incessant clamor of the telephone, and as a desire to return to the simple golden days of classicism. Our yearnings are not always consistent, but are likely to resemble that of the famous actor who said that, if given his choice of times to live, he would select the Victorian era, but with penicillin. Thoreau complained that the projected new telegraph from Maine to Texas was assumed to be indicative of progress, whereas Maine and Texas might well have nothing to communicate. Yet when the telegraph began to function Maine and Texas found that it helped to make them better parts of a stronger nation.

We need to learn to adapt to change, to behave like the surfboard rider who, poised in dynamic equilibrium, is shifting his weight ceaselessly to meet the impacts of a hundred buffeting waves. Meeting these impacts successfully makes men more human. The king crab has had a fairly static security for the past hundred and sixty million years, and remains a king crab. Some of his distant forebears who developed the ability to find dynamic security in a changing environment became the remote ancestors of men. We must progress from being children playing on a raft anchored in a smooth pond, to being surfboard riders able to hold ourselves composed and poised above the buffeting currents of life.

The question may fairly be raised as to how rapidly mankind should be expected to adapt to change. In particular, the new release of energy from the atom, with the increased threat of destruction from the sky that this makes possible, seems to many to be a freeing by scientists of a host of troubles on the world that we might well have been spared. Some laymen even believe that we have A-bombs and H-bombs because several brilliant physicists decided to sit down and invent a super-weapon. Having done this and been successful beyond their greatest expectations, they found that there is no getting the djin back into the bottle. This is far from the truth. The djin was getting out of the bottle anyway, and he is, in fact, a benevolent, constructive, and very obedient djin, whose faults are almost entirely those of his masters. Certainly we have no evidence that he is inherently more evil than his brothers who control fire, or electricity, or the blessed radiance of the sun.

Is energy from the sun man's servant, and that from the atom his master? Such a distinction is nonsense, and comes from men who fear that which they do not understand.

Those philosophers who wish we had killed off "materialistic science" in its infancy would have had us stop it with Becquerel in 1896, when the first explosion of a radioactive atom was observed. But this, alas, would still have been too late, for atoms have been exploding since the beginning of time, and all the sunlight that has kept the world alive comes from a thermo-nuclear reactor in the heavens. Pushed back to its ultimate, this cry of some humanists is revealed as a plea for ignorance. Science is merely the systematic search for truth by observation, and the interpretation of what is observed to aid in the finding and assimilation of more truth. We must take science as a whole or not at all, for one cannot shut his eyes to the truth at will and open them only whenever a philosopher says, "Now you may look."

The H-bomb is an extension of man's ability to exert mechanical and thermal forces, and belongs with the lever, the wheel, the steam engine, the tractor, and the diesel locomotive, in the category of energy converters that provide pushes and pulls at man's direction. It is merely an extreme example of one of man's amplifying and control mechanisms. Of itself it involves no more morality than any other machine. Only when we come to the question of what men do with electric motors and H-bombs do moral questions enter. Whether I push my fellow from his path or resist his push, with my unaided hand, a club, a rifle, or an atomic bomb, is merely a matter of degree. H-bombs pose new problems to humanity, to be sure, and the scientist shares the responsibility for their solution, but he could not make the problem less by closing his eyes and saying, "Look, folks, atoms don't explode. As you have long been aware, they are permanent and hard."

Man has always lived in the midst of forces that could easily overwhelm him. There is no discipline of knowledge that does not contain frightening revelations, from that of the ship designer who knows what two improperly approaching waves could do to his staunchest vessel, to the microscopist who catches glimpses of an otherwise invisible world of bacteria. But the cave man was frightened as thoroughly and much more often than we. Every human being has always lived in a balance so delicate that a slight shift could terminate his mortal existence in seconds. Yet men have grown accustomed to this, plan useful happy lives, write great books, paint and compose masterpieces, living always within a finger's breadth of the ultimate catastrophe.

How aware of its environment should a creature be? One answer is, "As aware as will not interfere with its further progress." The surgeon who wonders whether to tell a patient that he has an incurable disease faces this problem. The lathe operators who were taken into the confidence of top management, and then could not work for worry about whether the company would get its needed bank loan, obviously had too much awareness. Laymen worry too much now about H-bombs, yet they should worry some. How much is too much? The old adage, "What the mind doth not know, the heart doth not grieve over," has point insofar as comfort is concerned, but is overdone in the old Cape Cod saying, "What you don't know about, don't hurt you none." Since time began creatures have been hurt most by things that they did not know about. We must not shrink from the age-old lesson that living entities evolve by facing their problems and rising above them. Man is no exception.

There is no evidence that human evolution is drawing to a close. Rather it is accelerating. The challenge presented by the new developments of science has appeared in different guise many times before. The H-bomb is epitomized in the story of Adam and Eve in the Garden of Eden. The serpent scientists have hissed their message into the ear of the statesmen Eves, and we look back with longing to our former state of innocence. It is natural for many to look ahead with dread to the results of the new knowledge that has come to us. It is our duty, as all through the ages, to transform this knowledge into wisdom.

At first a flame was a fearsome thing, yet man learned to tame fire nearly a hundred thousand years ago. Though it still gets out of control occasionally, most of us could not live today without its help in providing warmth and loosening the fibers of food that would otherwise be too difficult to digest. So will it be with the nuclear fires when they are brought under control. That they are a million times more energetic than molecular fires means that they can help man rise that much higher above the amoeba, become that much more human and superhuman. It is natural for men to be fearful in the presence of any great new power, but man has demonstrated in the past that he has an inherent stability that enables him to win through to higher levels of spiritual achievement. Removing science would remove one of the principal factors in this stability, for it teaches us that we can progress from being slaves of our environment to masters of our destinies.

4

The conclusions of the seer and the scientist regarding human origins and progress often seem irreconcilable. There has always been a conflict between the subjective and the objective approaches. Yet human wisdom comes through both avenues, and we must maintain as fair a balance as possible between the Observer Within and the Observer Without. That this can be done is made evident by the examples of great men all down the ages. Omar Khayyám, whose quatrains are renowned as much for their beauty as for their philosophy, was a great mathematician. Leonardo da Vinci, in the highest rank of artists, was the greatest scientist of half a millennium. Sir Isaac Newton was reverent and deeply religious.

The mystic operates primarily through feeling and contemplation, while the scientist is trained to keep anything but observation and reason out of his approach to truth. He wants to analyze the universe dispassionately, as though he himself didn't exist. He is trained to admit that he does not know the answer to a problem when this is the case. To the mystic the answer comes first, and he may clothe his perception of intrinsic truth in wrappings that will not always stand up to close scientific scrutiny. A flowing river cannot be carried about in jugs, yet ideas are often all we have in which to transport the truth. We are likely to think the shape of the jug a property of the fluid it contains.

The accomplishments of Christopher Columbus are usually symbolized for schoolchildren in the statement that he proved that the world was round. This has given most Americans the impression that everyone before Columbus though that the world was flat. In point of fact its roundness was accepted by the average educated Greek nineteen hundred years before, and its size was measured correctly to within four percent by Eratosthenes in 250 B.C. To be sure, the schools have in recent years learned that giving Leif Erikson some credit does not detract from the glory of Columbus, but how many of us could list the five or six great explorers who landed on our shores before either? Columbus' great exploit was that he delivered up a new continent to a world that was ready for it. A special packet of ideas has been fitted up to symbolize this.

Men tend to believe what they want to believe. This makes us prone to accept belief in things that we especially wish to come about, things that we strongly fear, and things that seem to us especially appropriate. Our daily lives are conditioned much more than we realize by uncritical acceptance of concepts that sound logical and ring true.

As a simple journalistic example, consider that marvelous insect, the deer fly. When a popular writer wishes to discuss some subject, he looks up what has been written by others about it. If his subject is the speeds of living creatures, he is sure to read in many places of the deer fly as the fastest living thing. Even scientists accepted for years without question the statement that the deer fly flits at 800 miles an hour, until an especially thoughtful chemist, Irving Langmuir, decided to look into the matter. Langmuir was worried about the amount of energy that a tiny insect would have to store in his body to travel at so terrific a rate, to say nothing of the heat generated by air friction on the poor fly's head. He accordingly hunted up some deer flies, which do indeed flit about at amazing speed, and measured their rate of travel. This turned out to be about 70 miles an hour. He then traced the 800-mile figure through numerous references back to its original source, and found that it began with a parson-naturalist, who on one of his Monday walks became much impressed by the speed of flitting deer flies. This innocent lover of nature made a simple estimate, which unfortunately became colored by sentiment, and published his observation that the deer fly flew at 800 miles an hour. Since this was much faster than any other person had ever claimed any other animal to move, after having been copied several times it became a world's record. Though the story is ridiculous on its face, it was accepted by scientist and layman alike without question for years.

Today, long after Langmuir debunked the deer fly with wide publicity, it continues as often as before to be credited with ten times the speed it deserves. In fact, the most recently published table of flying speeds I have seen, circulated to an estimated fifty million readers, cited the male deer fly as traveling at 818 miles an hour, while the female did a paltry 800. Thus was introduced a pungent element of sex appeal that should carry the story on for additional decades.

In his attempts to battle ignorance with the weapons of reason the scientist is sometimes insensitive to human feelings. In smashing a truth-containing vessel because it has distorted its precious contents beyond what he considers all recognition, he may do a great disservice to mankind. The biologist who, in his search for simplicity and unity, looks for the basic essence of man in his bodily evolution, finds much to illuminate our understanding of the universe. But he must be careful not to get into the position of an amateur mechanic who, on looking into a television set to find out what it is, finds nothing there but glass and copper wires and metal tubes. To limit our concept of a television set to the sum of all its atoms is useful in certain circumstances, but it completely ignores the fact that the whole can be far greater than the sum of all its parts—in this case a whole that can bring sound and sight from the limits of the earth.

One can imagine the feelings of a clergyman who reads in a scientific book that the human mind does not exist! Dwelling within his own mind, he feels the scientist author to be a fool, obviously deluded and perhaps malevolent. Yet the scientist has a point. A psychologist who objects to the concept of a "mind" as something apart from the human brain, does so because he knows that this idea can get one into the same kind of trouble with facts that physicists got into when they started talking about a "luminiferous Aether." To visualize waves of heat and light traveling across empty space is foreign to our thought; therefore, to carry them, physicists imagined a new kind of matter, which they called the Aether. But when they started attributing to this Aether the properties of any other kind of matter with which humans are familiar, they were led to predict a behavior of beams of light that contradicted happenings that anyone could observe. The mistake lay in thinking that waves could only be carried by matter. To this day we do not know what else they can be carried by, but the Aether has now been junked, and physicists talk about warped space, the fourth dimension, and relativity. They feel much happier because more unknown parts of the universe have been brought into relation with parts we know, without leading to contradictions in thought.

So it is with the mind. Thinking of a "mind" apart from a brain has led to predictions that the scientist feels have not been experimentally verified. Though theories of the mind are not nearly so well worked out as the Theory of Relativity, in the sense of relating thought processes to the remainder of man's experience, there is no reason for the scientist and the mystic to consider themselves poles apart in this, so long as each avoids the dangers pointed out by the other.

To improve this situation, we need better communication. Many scientists today are making special efforts to humanize themselves. Many humanists are familiarizing themselves with the potentialities of science. On the other hand, there are many real lovers of mankind who still reveal a lack of understanding of the purposes, methods, and achievements of science. In his preface to *St. Joan*, Shaw says: "The mediaeval doctors of divinity who did not pretend to settle how many angels could dance on the point of a needle cut a very poor figure as far as romantic credulity is concerned beside the modern physicists who have settled to the billionth of a millimetre every movement and position in the dance of the electrons. . . . why the men who believe in electrons should regard themselves as less credulous than the men who believed in angels is not apparent to me."

The great difference that Shaw missed is that the men who believe in electrons are able to make demonstrably correct predictions here and now as a result. They are able to prophesy that if you will lead a flight of electrons across the vacuum of an X-ray tube in such and such a way, you will obtain rays that may enable you to destroy a tumor that is sapping the life of a human being. This, to be sure, is only one kind of prophecy. Angels have their place, just as electrons do. But the credulity of scientists is far from romantic in the sense that Shaw envisioned. They have developed a wholly modern method of prophecy, which they call quantitative extrapolation, which enables them to predict new types of interaction between matter and energy. Without this man would inevitably have had to remain less human than he is, and far less human than he can become.

The world is making great progress in tolerance. I went one year to Pisa on a pilgrimage to honor a personal debt to the memory of Galileo. I saw his leaning tower, and visited the region where he was kept in house arrest by Pope Urban VIII because he had insisted that the universe did not revolve around the earth. A day or two later, with a group of astronomers I listened to Pope Pius XII, whose deep spirituality was apparent even to those of us not of his faith. The Pope spoke well on the importance of scientific astronomy to the world, and I thought of him as making amends on behalf of his Church for its persecution of a great scientist because he defended one view of truth, which at that time had seemed to the Church to imperil an even more important view. After the address the Pope held an audience, and while shaking hands was asked by a brash young astronomer, "Is there life on Mars?" Eyes twinkling, the Pope replied, "How should I know?" Thus, in five hundred years, two paths in search of truth came closer together.

Science, a product of human experience distilled in a particular way, contains nothing intrinsically corrosive to the human spirit. I shall hope to show that most of the dangers feared from science by some humanists do not exist. There is overwhelming evidence that man's scientific achievements with material things can and, because of his nature, will, in the long run, contribute greatly to his spiritual welfare. Without such achievements, in fact, he could not reach the full flowering of his capabilities. Only does trouble arise when he attempts to substitute a worship of material things for those matters of the spirit on which his welfare ultimately depends.

5

Hazlitt wrote: "Man is the only animal that laughs and weeps, for he is the only animal that is struck by the difference between what things are and what they ought to be." The methods of science give the most powerful tools yet discovered for changing things to what they ought to be from what they are. Supplementing our other sources of knowledge, science can also help us decide what things are right, for we learn from experience, and science is the systematic production and analysis of experience. Yet always the conclusions of science must be informed and enriched, and to some extent modified, by the total wisdom of man.

In his search for truth the follower of science often becomes aware of beauty indescribably greater than his imagination could picture in advance. The ardor of the creative artist fills the scientist too when he pursues a discovery, and hopes for the perception of previously unknown truth. "Beauty is truth, truth beauty," said Keats, and science is the systematic search for truth.

This sweep and play of beauty extends throughout the whole of science. Consider the evolution of life on earth. This concept, now well proved, has nothing to do with belief in God, though it has been upsetting in the past to many persons pained by the cracking of the carapace of an inflexible theological dogma. The inspiring prospect of the upward progress of life over millions of years stirs emotions equal to those produced by the most sublime music and poetry. Scientists who have seen the great paintings in the Sistine Chapel and the Louvre, and have felt that tingling in the spinal cord that comes from observation of truly great art, have received the same inner thrill from observing that when a bird sits on a bough, a tiny locking bone in his foot clamps his claws around the perch so that his muscles can relax without danger of his falling when asleep. The God who is said to note each sparrow's fall also built something into a proton that keeps the sparrow from falling. To some the latter concept is even more comforting than the former.

In the following pages we shall examine, among other aspects of science, its humanizing effect. To become more human means not merely to become more spiritual; I would want a man rather to become of greater stature and awareness in his material, emotional, mental, and spiritual structures together. Above all, he should bring all these aspects of his personality into proper balance and proportion. In aiding such growth, science takes its place beside religion and art as one of the great humanizing influences of mankind.

In discussing the physical aspects of man's advancement, I shall hope to be held free of accusations of materialism. We live in a universe that is progressing, and one purpose of this book is to convey a sense of the endless possibilities of this progress. The accumulation of experience results in an uneven but definite increase in the spiritual qualities that are of most importance to man—truth, justice, love, humility, integrity, and all the rest. Spiritual values distill slowly from the interaction of sensation, emotion, and thought, which depend in turn on man's physical body, which is formed by his environment, which depends ultimately on the properties of matter. Science has effects on each of these. Even if one wishes to picture what we call the eternal values as abstract concepts superposed on the character of man from without (and I do not quarrel with this, though I feel that it detracts from the beauty and integrity of the unified picture), man certainly has the power of developing spiritual qualities, and how he does so is basically affected by his physical experience. One purpose of science is to codify and illumine this experience.

The grandeur of human destiny becomes really manifest only when man is released to some extent from the battle for physical existence, and learns that on a constantly widening scale he can become a small creator. "Build thee more stately mansions, O my soul," sang Holmes, and science aids religion and art in making this literally possible.

Let us make our approach to science, then, the human one. Our great interest is in man, and we can see man best, in all his humanness and incipient godliness, against the background of progressing nature. Perhaps by this means we may reach some realization of what man has been, why we are here, and, most important, what man may be.

Chapter Two

The Control of Matter

Though man does not live by bread alone, he must have bread to live. The availability of all the sorts of bread that feed man's body, his mind, and his spirit depend upon matter and on man's ability to control it.

Human beings have always lacked materials suitable for doing some of the things they wanted to do most. Leonardo da Vinci, born five hundred years too soon, had to construct his wonderful machines of leather and wood for lack of metals and plastics and rubber. We have much more to do with than he, yet we are impatient because glass is not flexible, because a sheet of plastic is readily scratched, and because no substance has been found which does not melt or corrode in the interior of our hottest engines.

It is natural to think that there has been just so much matter on earth since its beginning, and that with this man must make do, except for a few meteorites that hit the earth now and then. Although this is true of the basic atoms of which all matter is composed, the creation of new substances still goes on rapidly. When atoms are arranged in a new pattern to form a molecule which proves to be stable, a new material results. Unaided nature has not yet had opportunity to try all the arrangements of atoms that make stable molecules, and man can speed this process greatly. Hundreds of new kinds of such molecules are being designed successfully each day in the chemical laboratories of the world. The availability of a single new material that results from such work, a new DDT or atabrine or penicillin, can mean life itself to millions of people.

Chemists, until recent years, made their experiments pretty much at random, testing whatever new substances turned up in their fizzing mixtures to see whether they would be useful as drugs or insecticides or plastics, or would fill any of a thousand other human needs. As they learn more about how atoms and molecules are built, however, they can carry out experiments in the molecular world with their eyes more fully open. In many cases they can create new materials by design, tailoring a molecule to produce a substance having special properties, or refitting old molecules to special needs. In fact, chemists have now constructed more new varieties of molecules than they have found in nature, and they are practically sure in future to produce thousands of times as many new substances as they have made thus far.

Among the molecules that man has himself produced are some of his greatest benefactors. Atabrine and primaquine turn out to be better than nature's quinine to cure malaria. The use of DDT for killing flies has doubled the milk produced by the dairy herds of a nation. Other new substances, such as Freon and butyl rubber and cellulose acetate, have added greatly to man's social wealth, one by making practicable a better refrigerator, the second by reducing the leakage of air from auto tires, and the third by giving the moving-picture industry a fire-resisting film base. Each of these substances can also perform other useful chores. To a philosopher these materials may seem unimportant milestones on the path to truth, but they are by-products of man's closer approach to reality.

Today a list of the known kinds of molecules would contain more than a million entries, and these are being added to at the rate of about thirty thousand a year. In the laboratories of one large chemical firm it is considered a poor day when at least one special new substance is not discovered that is worth following up to see if it can be made useful. Given long names that are perplexing to most of us but describe their atomic arrangements to chemists, popular new molecules soon become known by trade or nicknames. Many of these become household words, like aspirin and Benzedrine.

The modern refrigerator owes much of its success to twenty-five cents' worth of a special molecule custom-built for the purpose. Each refrigerator needs a few ounces of a vapor which can be compressed at ordinary temperatures to liquid form, cooled off with an electric fan, and then evaporated by absorbing heat from foodstuffs. All the vapors tried were found either to be hard to liquefy, or to boil at the wrong temperature, or to be noxious or toxic or corrosive. After concluding that no molecule with exactly the right properties existed in nature, chemists decided to make one. They found that carbon tetrachloride, the common cleaning fluid, whose molecules each consist of four chlorine atoms clustered around a carbon atom, was almost suitable, but its molecules were slightly too heavy, and the material was poisonous if breathed in quantity. So they removed two of the chlorine atoms from each molecule and replaced them with two lighter fluorine atoms. The new molecule thus formed, which they named Freon, was found to fill the bill to perfection. Now more than four million refrigerators containing it are sold each year in the United States. These are much better refrigerators than the two hundred thousand that were sold in 1926, and a unit of the same size as an earlier one costs only about half as much.

Like men, molecules destined to become famous sometimes remain unappreciated for many years. Dichlorodiphenyltrichlorethane, a cryptic name that bares to the initiated a complex molecular structure, was first made by a student in Germany in 1874. It languished in a bottle on the shelf as just another chemical substance until a Swiss chemist, when World War II was starting, found that contact with it caused many sorts of insects to go into a buzzing dance of death. Now 100 million pounds are sold each year as DDT. In four years this substance nearly doubled the yield of potatoes in Maine by killing beetles. In Ceylon, its use for mosquito control soon cut the death rate in half. In Sardinia, it reduced malaria from ten thousand new cases in 1945 to three new cases in 1951. In New Guinea during World War II it was an effective weapon, for in the Japanese army the malaria rate exceeded 95 percent for all troops in the area while malaria was held in the U.S. Army to well below 1 percent.

More than ten thousand varieties of insects, ticks, and mites cause four billion dollars' worth of damage each year in the United States, and DDT is lethal to many of them. To be sure, house flies have now begun in certain regions to develop immunity, just as men can develop a tolerance for arsenic and finally come to depend upon it. In a few places mosquitoes also are showing some resistance, apparently, like the flies, selectively developing in succeeding generations an enzyme molecule that combines with the DDT molecule and effectively pulls its fuse. But this need not discourage us, for chemists are developing a whole arsenal of new insecticides, and thousands more await discovery. A simple molecule called benzene hexachloride is found to be lethal to insects if its chlorine atoms are fitted into a certain pattern. Another, methoxychlor, is a specialist molecule that can be used to kill insects that bother cows, without getting into the milk as DDT does. Discriminating use of such materials can be expected to keep insects increasingly in hand, for whenever a species develops immunity to one toxic molecule, another can be made available to hold it in check.

Even when a useful molecule can be found in natural substances, as is caffeine in coffee and tea, it is sometimes cheaper to synthesize it from simpler materials. This is now the case not only with caffeine, but also with ethyl alcohol (the drinking kind), acetic acid as in vinegar, glycerine as in nitroglycerine and cosmetics, Vitamin C as in orange juice, and many other molecules. Ninety-nine percent of all dyes are today built up from atoms taken from coal tar. Ninety-five percent of plastics are synthetic, 75 percent of drugs, 65 percent of rubber products, 50 percent of paints, and 20 percent of textile fibers. These percentages are bound to go up as men learn more about handling atoms to produce new molecules. And we must not think of the synthetic molecules as substitutes of lower quality.

The prejudice against "chemicals" produced by men fitting atoms together, as being in some way inferior to "natural" substances, arose because of the likelihood, in earlier times, that the chemist either could not duplicate a molecule exactly, or that he would omit from a mixture some important substance whose presence he had not detected, such as a vitamin or a hormone. Now the methods by which chemists can analyze a substance and determine how all the atoms of its components are arranged have been greatly improved, and the curse is being lifted from the word "synthetic." When the chemist does his work properly, the substances he makes are often superior to those produced in nature, in being more specifically suited for a purpose. After all, the cinchona tree did not develop quinine in its bark to kill malaria germs.

2

Many billions of dollars' worth of molecules of kinds that did not exist twenty years ago are now sold in the United States each year. Since 1635, when John Winthrop, Jr., began to manufacture saltpeter and alum in Massachusetts, the chemicals industry has grown to be the sixth largest in America, and furnishes employment for millions of men. Every useful new type of molecule means a new set of jobs.

One new substance of importance often gives rise to a multimillion-dollar industry in only a few years. The long list of those that have done so includes nylon, cellulose acetate, cellulose nitrate, 2,4-D, DDT, tetraethyl lead, polystyrene, polyethylene, methyl methacrylate and several synthetic rubbers. The plastics, textile, drug, aerosol, fertilizer, pest control, and detergent industries are all expanding rapidly as new molecules that are found useful in their processes become available.

To see how new materials affect our standard of living, consider the rubber used in automobile tires. In 1910, an American workman could expect to drive twenty miles on the rubber he could purchase with an hour's work. Today he can drive more than one hundred times as far. His wealth level in terms of the actual cost of rubber has improved sixteen-fold, but since he is also more productive because he can control energy more effectively, he can now earn six times as much in an hour. In addition, his tires travel farther because they are used on better roads.

With X-rays, physicists and chemists have found the twisted molecules in various kinds of rubbers to be arranged in tiny helices, like spiral springs stitched together with atomic bonds in cross-linked chains that give unique properties of stretch and toughness. To an elastic molecular back-bone, strong atomic side branches can be grafted which add tenacity without loss of resilience. Resistance to abrasion can be built in with added sulfur and carbon atoms. An auto-mobile tire is made of little but carbon and hydrogen atoms, yet how much more it is than a mixture of coal dust with an explosive gas! Far more important than the substance of matter is its form, its organization into patterns. Careful arranging of the atoms in rubber gives resilient molecular springs that confer entirely new properties on the matter made from them. But displace some of the atoms from their proper positions and you are likely to get gutta-percha instead of rubber, or only a mass of sticky mudlike goo.

Dozens of new kinds of rubbers can now be synthesized. Instead of the original "rubber" taken from the sap of the Hevea tree, at first believed useful only to rub out pencil marks, we have many specialist rubbers, one best for rain-coats, another for inner tubes that lose air more slowly than does natural rubber, another to plug leaks, and others for tough tire treads and side walls. Where would our fifty-eight million motor cars be without rubber tires?

It is important to remember that most of the new mole-cules are made by putting together relatively simple and readily available atoms. Water furnishes all the hydrogen and oxygen we need, air gives oxygen and nitrogen, petro-leum and coal give carbon, limestone gives calcium. Ninety percent of the earth's crust is made up of these and ten other light and useful varieties of atoms.

A great family of materials made of such common atoms is the plastics. Their molecules do not stretch much, but when heated a little, or partially dissolved in other molecules, they can be made to flow into any desired shape, and will then set firmly into place to hold this shape. We use five billion dollars' worth of plastics products each year, and soon more plastics will be used as building materials, a field in which they already compete with glass and aluminum, though still behind wood and steel.

Plastics shaped into large pieces are finding vast new markets. Plastic water pipe, now extruded by the mile from polyethylene, resists bursting nearly as well as welded steel pipe, is much lighter, and does not rust or corrode. However, this pipe cannot be used for hot liquids, and is rather easily bruised. We need a plastic as flexible as those we now have, but with the surface hardness of glass. The closest approach to this so far is in the safety glass used in windshields, a sandwich of alternate layers of glass and plastic that cling firmly together. It would be even more useful to combine the properties of the two on the molecular level.

Many plastics can be made much stronger by hooking together additional atomic bonds between their molecules. When newly pressed from flax seeds, the molecules of linseed oil, for example, hang together loosely in chains, with few of their atomic bonds cross-hitched to bind the chains in bundles and sheets. When paint that contains linseed oil dries, its molecules harden in cross-linked chains with oxygen molecules from the air, and it forms into a tough and hard skin. By shining light on the linseed oil, or by heating and stirring it in the presence of oxygen, such polymerization can be increased.

Nuclear radiations, of the sort produced in a modern uranium pile or a high-voltage atom smasher, have recently been found useful to effect greater polymerization. Fast neutrons from a pile can in a short time change a plastic bottle that collapses in warm water into one that will stand nearly twice the temperature. These rays apparently knock atoms out of crucial points in the molecular structure so that additional atomic bonds are jarred to link together. A single fast-moving neutron can induce as many as five thousand

atoms to join electronic hands to strengthen the plastic structure. Yet the neutron was discovered only in 1932, and was
predicted theoretically by several physicists before it was
looked for and found. Perhaps we shall learn to beat parts
of our atomic bombs into tougheners for tire treads, and a
great new plastics industry will spring up about the uranium
pile.

Especially useful are certain plastics which when dissolved
can be squeezed through tiny holes to form strong textile
filaments, a process long ago perfected by the silkworm and
the spider. One of the most successful of these is nylon.
Eighty million American women now buy more than six
hundred million pairs of nylon stockings a year.

One of the early attempts to produce a filament stronger
and more resilient than silk resulted in rayon. This, made
from a molecule already used for motion picture film base,
for cellophane, and for some types of plastic squeeze bottles,
gave a fiber useful for many purposes but it did not solve
the hosiery problem. After much research the nylon molecule was developed, and was found to give, after stretching to
line up the molecules, a tougher elastic fiber. Nylon has
now been joined by a host of other plastics that can be spun
into textile fibers, each formed from a new kind of molecule.

The material known as Teflon contains fluorine atoms that
make it tough, and its molecules hold fast to those of dyes
that otherwise fade in sunlight, so it serves well for awnings
and drapes. Orlon, Dynel, Acrilan, Dacron each have their
own advantages, and to the fibers that we obtain from nature—cotton, wool, silk, flax, and hemp—the chemist has now
added dozens made from molecules that he assembled himself. This type of material progress will appear more important to the humanist later, when the world comes to need
all of its productive land to raise foodstuffs. Then millions

of families may have to choose between being rationed on
cotton, or on extra babies.

3

Some seventy of the atoms of the chemical elements, most
of them metals like copper and iron and gold, can form substances directly without the intermediate production of molecules. In a molecule the atoms cluster in a pattern, while in
a metallic crystal they may hang together directly in chains
and lattices, sheets and blocks, in almost endless repetition.
When something, usually a concentration of foreign atoms,
occurs to stop the extension of the lattice, a new crystal may
be started that extends in a slightly different direction, separated from the other by a grain boundary. Controlling the
atoms in such grain boundaries can have a great effect on the
strength of a bar of metal.

Carbon atoms, which have an outer structure consisting
of four electrons arranged at the points of a pyramid, build
up crystals in several different ways. In one arrangement
they form crystals of graphite, which are soft, black, and
act as a good lubricant. In another, exactly the same atoms
form diamond, brilliant, transparent, and the hardest substance known. Thus the properties of a material depend not
only on the atoms of which it is composed, but on the patterns in which they are arranged.

A solid formed from a mass of metal crystals, such as an
iron bar, can often be altered in its properties by mixing into
its material while molten a definite concentration of other
atoms to change the crystal lattice that forms on cooling.
In this way iron can be alloyed with carbon to make steel,
a simple fact that makes the machine age possible. If chromium and other atoms are added to iron in proper propor-

tions, stainless steel that resists corrosion can be formed. The hair spring of a watch must be strong and of uniform elasticity, able to push back gently against the balance wheel so as to reverse its motion five times each second. It is expected to do this more than three billion times in the lifetime of the watch it serves. Thus its atoms must be reliably fitted together, and any weak spots between crystals must be strengthened with such atoms as chromium, silicon and vanadium.

Only about half of the metals we know of are now used in industry. The others are either too rare, or too expensive to purify. Often all that is needed to make an expensive metal cheaper is to discover how it can be used effectively. Titanium, frequently referred to as the "new wonder metal," is an atom known for more than one hundred and fifty years, and is actually the ninth most abundant metal atom in the earth's surface. Combined with iron and oxygen as ilmenite, it colors black many of the beach sands of Australia and elsewhere.

Until recently titanium in metal form was produced only in very small quantities, and cost approximately $3,000 a pound to make. Long considered too brittle to be useful, shortly after World War II it was found that titanium can be formed into strong and ductile sheets if the number of atoms of impurities in it are reduced to less than one atom to each five hundred titanium atoms. Demand soon brought the price down to four dollars and seventy-five cents a pound, but this is still expensive compared to aluminum at twenty-two cents a pound, and steel at three cents. Nevertheless, at temperatures above 700°F a sheet of titanium is stronger than one of either steel or aluminum of the same weight, and it resists corrosion better even than stainless steel. Thus using titanium can save several hundred pounds in the weight of an airplane, and it is now replacing other metals in many such applications. Other metals which are at present expensive are doubtless destined similarly to be put into the service of man, and thousands of alloys still await testing by the metallurgist.

The strength and other properties of a metal depend to a surprising degree on its purity. One atom of oxygen among a million of copper can greatly affect both the strength of a piece of copper wire and its ability to conduct electricity, for these properties depend on the regularity in arrangement of the atoms that compose its crystals. These atoms line up like vast regiments of soldiers in almost endless ranks. Inserting a dancing girl into the midst of a marching rank of two hundred soldiers might be expected to affect their ability to maneuver. If placed in front of a regiment of a hundred columns and a hundred ranks, one damsel could easily disrupt the attention of ten thousand men. The ranks of atoms run in three-dimensions, and a single oxygen atom can disarrange a cube of copper containing 200 by 200 by 200 atoms. Thus one foreign atom of irregular size, exerting unusual forces, may disrupt the ranks of eight million atoms, and change the properties of the crystal that they form.

Some of the desirable new applications of metals depend on the very rapid changes that occur as the last traces of impurities, one foreigner among a billion or more native atoms, are removed. To produce good germanium for transistors, the effective substitutes for many electronic vacuum tubes, foreign atoms must be driven out until not more than one remains in each group of ten billion germanium atoms. Then, with far more delicate admixture than that used by the chef who touches the salad bowl with a clove of garlic, each hundred million atoms of germanium are seasoned with one antimony atom. Here the whole action of the transistor regiment depends on the presence of the dancing girl.

How long can our supplies of atoms be expected to last, before they are used up? Our mines can eventually be expected to give out, and as the concentration of such ores as

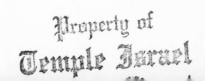

those of copper and tin and lead diminishes, the amount of energy needed to gather useful atoms will increase. Fortunately our supplies of energy are increasing even more rapidly, and we should never really run out of atoms, for we do not lose any or use them up—we merely scatter them, or bind them in various molecules from which they can later be recovered. When the world's mines eventually fail, there is always the sea.

Though not all the chemical elements are found in sea water, those most essential for living are there. The salt content of the sea varies from less than 1 percent in parts of the Baltic to more than 4 percent in sections of the Mediterranean, but on the average there are 3½ pounds of dissolved chemicals in every 100 pounds of ocean. In each cubic mile of Atlantic sea water are 166 million tons of useful atoms, apart from hydrogen and oxygen—143 million tons of table salt containing valuable sodium and chlorine atoms; 5 million tons of magnesium; 300,000 tons of bromine; and 18 million tons of some fifty other assorted elements. There is even five million dollars' worth of gold, but this would at present cost three hundred billion dollars to get out, and we need many other atoms much more than gold.

There is great hope that cheaper methods will be found than those now available to separate solids from sea water, which at present cost about one dollar a thousand gallons. One good method appears to be to use an electrical filter. Thin membranes of certain types can be made to pass only positively charged molecules, while others pass only negatively charged molecules, which makes it possible to concentrate metallic materials between them. When we have plenty of cheap energy, as will probably be true when the nuclear age really starts to blossom, mining the sea should be increasingly worthwhile.

4

As we have noted, all of our million or so known kinds of molecules are composed of different arrangements of only eighty-eight kinds of atoms. Most of them, in fact, are made of atoms of only a dozen or so varieties. And these atoms consist in turn only of various assembly patterns of the three basic particles—protons, neutrons, and electrons—held together by forces not yet perfectly understood. All of our material world results from the interaction of electric, magnetic, and gravitational forces among these particles, and all our life experiences are based on such interactions. As we understand them better, we come to better understanding of ourselves.

If more than half of our molecules are new within the century, how old are the atoms of which they are made? Most of these have probably been around for at least five billion years, or since a little before the world was born. But the particles of which the atoms are composed have probably existed much longer.

According to one theory now widely accepted, our universe, including all the galaxies that we can see with the strongest telescope, began to take on its present form between five and ten billion years ago, with a tremendous explosion. At Time Zero primordial matter had shrunk to a dense tremendous ball of protons and neutrons, which repelled each other electrically so strongly that they were unable to stick together to form the nuclei of atoms. Our universe was yet unborn. Then something gave, a cataclysmic explosion occurred, and the great globe blew up. The resulting spreading of matter is still going on; we can see many millions of galaxies like our own, some as far as six thousand million million million miles away, receding from each other at thousands of miles a second as the universe expands.

The creation of matter as we know it apparently occurred during the first few minutes of this explosion. As they collided at high speed neutrons and protons were combined into many patterns that proved stable, so that countless nuclei of light atoms like oxygen and carbon were formed. Then, in regions where temperatures of a billion degrees or more were produced, even more complex nuclei were built up by adding neutrons and protons to these light nuclei. It is believed that within a short time after the explosion started practically all of the complex natural atomic nuclei we know had been formed, including the heaviest, uranium, and perhaps some even heavier.

Thinking of ourselves for the moment as creators assigned to build up atoms for a new world, we can visualize a supply of protons and one of neutrons, from which we are to assemble all possible different nuclear patterns. Some of these nuclei will not hold together for long, but others will be extremely stable. Each, when allowed to gather around itself a number of electrons equal to the number of protons in it, will become an atom.

First we try a single proton, and this, when it picks up an electron, becomes a hydrogen atom. Then we put a proton and a neutron together; this nucleus still can hold only one electron, so it too is hydrogen, but of a heavier kind, deuterium. A proton and two neutrons, forming tritium, gives still heavier hydrogen, but is only moderately stable. Two protons and a neutron, light helium, likewise explode apart soon after we form a nucleus from them. But when we come to two protons and two neutrons a very stable nucleus is formed, which gathers two electrons to become the atom of the now familiar gas helium.

So we go on up through all the possible combinations of

nucleons, a term for the protons and neutrons of which nuclei are composed. We find that in general those nuclei are most stable in which the number of protons is about equal to the number of neutrons. Especially stable are those that contain 2, 8, 20, 28, 50, 82, and 126 nucleons. But as we get up to very heavy atoms, such as uranium, with 92 protons and 146 neutrons, more and more of the nuclei we produce are unstable, and blow up soon after they are put together. Before we are done we have made about a thousand kinds of atomic nuclei, most of them fairly stable. But many of these are isotopes, atomic species that differ only in having nuclei of different masses, but with the same numbers of protons in their nuclei, and hence the same numbers of electrons in their external structures. Thus they behave alike in forming molecules, and out of our thousand isotopes we get only a hundred different chemical elements.

A number of these elements are so unstable that their atoms last only seconds or hours. This explains why only 88 varieties are found in nature. Recently, however, many missing kinds of atoms, especially those with from 93 to 101 external electrons, have been made by man. None of the man-made atoms is permanent, and in making them scientists have merely been repeating the production of exploding atoms that nature has carried out many times before.

Even the isotopes found in nature contain a large fraction that are unstable, that is radioactive, so that they explode after a time. Even if one could watch a given atom one could not predict just when it would blow up, but a million of any variety can be definitely predicted to be reduced to half a million within a definite time, called the "half-life" of that atomic species. Thus a pound of U 235, the active uranium isotope, will be reduced to half a pound in seven hundred million years, and to a quarter pound in seven hundred million more. Various isotopes have half-lives ranging from the fraction of a trillionth of a second of lithium 5 to the many billions of years of stable elements.

Thus while many of our atoms are over five billion years old, others are much younger, having been formed by the radioactive disintegration of heavier atoms. And now that man has learned how to produce one kind of atom from another, we have a nuclear super-chemistry in which particles are rearranged in nuclei, similar to that with which chemists have learned to rearrange atoms in molecules.

To change a stable atomic nucleus of one complex atom into that of a heavier one by heat alone is likely to require temperatures of hundreds of millions of degrees. In a volume of a few cubic yards at the center of an A-bomb explosion, a temperature of a hundred million degrees may be reached for a short time. This is sufficient to split atoms apart, transforming them by fission, as in the atomic bomb, but not enough to synthesize elements much heavier than helium. However, one atom at a time can be changed by shooting a nuclear particle at high speed into its nucleus. Once they have been forced close to each other, particles in a nucleus are clamped together by forces about a million times as great as those that hold the electrons in an atom or molecule. To knock an electron out of a hydrogen atom, one need only strike it with another electron that has fallen through a dozen accelerating volts; to knock a particle out of a helium nucleus requires that it be hit by a nuclear bullet that has fallen through more than 28 million volts. The more nucleons there are in a stable nucleus, the tighter they tend to cling together. To smash an iron nucleus requires 487 million electron volts; to smash a lead one, 1580 million.

To smash such nuclei on a small scale, with the object of seeing what happens rather than to transmute much material, physicists construct particle accelerators. These cyclotrons, synchrotrons, bevatrons, cosmotrons, and the like, which whirl charged subatomic particles around until they hurtle through space as if they had been dropped over electrical cliffs up to six billion volts high, give particles speeds equivalent to those they would have at the centers of hot and heavy stars.

Thus has man finally brought about the dream of the alchemist, the conversion of one element into another. To change the elements requires not chemical but super-chemical methods. The forces involved are about a million times as great as those envisaged by the alchemist, who worked largely by intuition, and the results achieved reveal a beauty and unity in nature of which he did not dream. No longer are atoms indivisible billiard balls, but little universes of the physicist, each a microcosm that opens up new wonders and capabilities to mankind.

Far more important than changing dross metals into gold is the possibility of changing any atom into any other. To-day, turning gold into mercury is more profitable than turning lead into gold, for it turns out to be a fine way of getting a supply of a special mercury isotope useful for burning in electric lamps to produce bright light of a needed sharply single color.

Even more important to mankind than the availability of nuclear energy will be the new informing of science that will result from the possibility of nuclear transformations. As the atomic age proceeds, our controls over matter will improve, not so much because we will get new kinds of atoms, as because we will better understand how to manipulate those we have. This new basic understanding gives man also better control over the world of molecules, and hence over the entire living world. Now, for example, we are better able to determine how plants use fertilizers. By putting in the plant food a radioactive isotope of one of the important atoms such as phosphorus, and following its exploding atoms from cell to living cell, we can see what the plant does with phosphorus. Exploding atoms can be detected with a Geiger counter in amounts a millionth of a millionth as great as those needed for the most sensitive chemical analysis.

By such means it will soon be possible to tell where all the kinds of atoms that make up a plant or animal travel about in it, and what ultimately becomes of them. "Hot" atoms behave chemically exactly as cold atoms do, and, if used only by thousands, need not hurt the organism into which they are introduced. By using them it has been found that many plants can absorb some fertilizers more quickly and effectively if these are applied to their leaves instead of their roots, a result quite unexpected. Again, radioactive sugar has been produced by letting plants grow in an atmosphere containing carbon dioxide made from carbon 14 atoms, an isotope that is strongly radioactive. When this sugar was fed to mice, within twenty-four hours they were found to have breathed out as carbon dioxide 85 percent of the exploding atoms, and hence of the ordinary carbon atoms in the sugar. Thus it becomes possible to get new insight into living processes, all of which are possible because of the properties possessed by matter.

5

The great diversity of materials that we find in nature springs from the variety of external structure patterns of the atoms of the chemical elements. This variety results from three basic factors. First, the number of electrons that an atom can contain is the number that will neutralize its nucleus electrically, and hence is equal to the number of protons in that nucleus. Second, these electrons, being attracted by the nucleus both electrically and magnetically, will swing into orbits about it as closely bound to it as they can get. Third, each electron is prevented from getting as close to the nucleus as the forces on it would otherwise direct, by the fact that it must take up such an orbital position, and spin in such a way, that it is doing at least one thing different from what each other electron in that atom is doing. This is a somewhat oversimplified statement of Pauli's Exclusion Principle, an aspect of the Quantum Theory that explains with great precision and beauty most of the observed properties of the different kinds of atoms, and shows why they can be arranged in a Periodic Table of the Elements in which these regularities in atomic characteristics can be observed.

It has long been known that atoms show family resemblances, the members of each group having somewhat similar combining properties with other atoms. Thus helium atoms, with only two electrons spinning in opposite directions, have their electric and magnetic forces so well balanced internally that they combine with no other atoms to form molecules, and a molecule of helium is merely an atom. Neon, argon, krypton, and xenon, with 10, 18, 36, and 54 electrons respectively, are similarly inert. Sodium atoms with 11 electrons have a single bond with which they can hook to other atoms, as do potassium, rubidium, and cesium, with 19, 37, and 55 electrons. Magnesium, with 12, behaves like calcium with 20, strontium with 38, and barium with 56, all of which have two atomic hooks. These sets of numbers have similar respective differences. Aluminum has three fastening points, or a triple valence, and carbon four. The properties of matter can be related to the numbers and kinds of the bonds among the atoms of which its molecules are composed.

The electric and magnetic forces between nuclei and electrons are not completely balanced in most molecules, and the residual forces cause neighboring molecules to hang together, if they are not vibrating with heat so rapidly as to break these

bonds. Though helium is so self-sufficient that it remains a
gas formed of single atoms down to extremely low temperatures, hydrogen atoms cling to each other or to fluorine atoms
so firmly that very high temperatures are needed to shake
them apart. The familiar water molecule, in which two hydrogen atoms and an oxygen cling firmly together, holds
strongly enough to its fellows to form a crystalline solid at
temperatures below 32°F, a sparkling liquid in the range of
living temperatures, and a gas at higher ones, without breaking apart. If these things were not so, man, a watery creature
at best, could not be what he is.

A given type of atom can combine with others to form
molecules having widely varying properties. Thus silicon,
an atom that combines with other silicon atoms to produce
metallic crystals, and with oxygen composes the basic part
of most sands and glasses, also enters importantly into many
improved oils, greases, cosmetics, paints, rubbers, resins, and
insulating materials, which are found to stand higher temperatures than similar molecules built with carbon atoms. Though
the silicon atom is like carbon in external electronic structure,
it lacks carbon's ability to form extremely long stable chains
of atoms. Thus silicon is of no use in building up the complex molecules of living matter.

Rearrangement of the atoms in a molecule usually produces striking changes in its properties. Molecules that contain the same atomic parts, but have these arranged in different
patterns, are called isomers. Eight hydrogen atoms, four carbon atoms, and two oxygen atoms assembled in one way
form the butyric acid molecule that gives the stench to rancid
butter. These same atoms arranged in a different pattern
form a molecule of ethyl acetate, which has a pleasantly fresh
odor. The same atoms that form in one isomer a useful drug,
may in another arrangement become a deadly poison. A
pattern consisting of forty-eight atoms of four different kinds

forms a quinine molecule, which kills the microorganisms in the blood that produce malaria. Rearranged these atoms form quinidine, a drug useful for its effect on the heart. Still other patterns called epiquine and epiquinidine have few known uses as yet.

There are more than a thousand different stable ways of arranging the atoms of carbon, hydrogen, and chlorine that make up a molecule of DDT, and most of these atomic patterns bother insects hardly at all; but arrange the atoms in one special pattern and you get a molecule that has killed insects by the trillions. Again, a large fraction of the joys and sorrows of mankind come from the action on the human body of the molecule called androgen. Change the pattern of the atoms in this sex hormone ever so slightly, and its possessor loses beauty, drive, ambition, and a hundred other traits of vital importance to living. Fortunately the forces holding atoms together into patterns, though flexible, are strong and stable.

Though chemists talk glibly about taking molecules apart, they usually handle them only by the trillions. It is difficult for us to picture how small a molecule really is, and various devices have been invented to emphasize their minuteness. Thus, there are many more molecules in a glass of water than there are glasses of water in all the oceans of the world. Or, if the molecules in one droplet of water were arranged in a single line as close together as possible, they would extend hundreds of times around the earth. Or again, if one were to count each atom in a pound of lead, and in imagination put these one by one into a dustpan until one had emptied a million dustpans of a million atoms each, and then did this a million times, one would have worked on only a millionth of the lead. Yet chemists are able to sort out atoms and to form new molecules quite dexterously. They do this by finding what environment is needed to induce a herd of atoms to combine naturally and automatically into the molecules that are desired. The forces that will hold the atoms together lie waiting to click them into stable patterns.

The chemist is, however, greatly frustrated at present because of his limited ability to control the exact patterns that atoms will take in forming a new molecule. For example, amino-acid molecules can be either left-handed or right-handed, as a spiral staircase can twist one way or the other. Strangely, nature uses mostly the left-handed ones in constructing the protein molecules useful for living cells, but when the chemist synthesizes amino-acids in a test tube he is likely to get equal amounts of the right- and left-handed varieties because he does not yet know how to drill the individual atoms into forming only the desired molecular patterns. Thus his process may be automatically limited to 50 percent efficiency or less, whereas nature, which gets at the individual atoms by means of enzymes, produces left-handed molecules one by one with left-handed molecular templates.

The story of modern chemistry shows us how matter has evolved, and evolves ever faster under the influence of human thought, from the simple to the more complex. But is complexity a desirable end of itself? asks the humanist. Chaotic complexity, No, answers the scientist, but ordered complexity is what makes possible all the wondrous possibilities of a rich and living world.

In the centers of giant stars matter is squashed to a mishmash of protons and neutrons. Under certain special conditions of temperature and pressure these can be ordered into atomic nuclei, which then collect electrons and form the atoms of the chemical elements. Under still more special conditions, which we shall look at later, these atoms collect into myriads of molecules, some so complex that they are able to come alive. Still greater capabilities come to matter when these molecules can join to form cells, and these associate into organs, and these in turn form living creatures that sense and feel and think. But before we can understand how this comes about, we must consider another basic stuff of the universe, energy, which informs matter, moves it, and can bring it finally to life.

Chapter Three

The Control of Energy

How many men can live on earth at once, and how long and fully they can live, depend on man's ability to control energy and matter. Those qualities of mind and spirit that give human life its sense and value cannot be developed until man has attained a certain minimal material standard of living. Philosophers may differ regarding how adequately a man should be fed, clothed, housed, protected, transported, educated, and entertained for his own best good, but the whole course of evolution shows that it is increased ability to control energy and matter that enables any creature to come increasingly alive.

Men who live on what they can gather from the woods, fields, and waters of the earth, such as the Australian aborigines, each need about two square miles of reasonably productive terrain in which to hunt, fish, or otherwise gather the energy needed to keep themselves alive. But the earth could support only twenty million persons in this way. By farming, that is by storing extra energy from sunlight in the leaves of plants through cultivation, two to five billion more persons can live on earth at once. Nearly two-thirds of humanity now depends on such an agricultural economy.

The remaining third of living people handle energy much more directly and efficiently. The Western World has developed an industrial economy with which the earth could be made to support in comfort and, if they would, in security at least fifty billion people, or twenty times the number now alive. Science and technology make living possible for many more human beings than could exist without them. If the developments of science that have produced the Machine Age were to be renounced, the world would be found already overfull.

In an economy in which of necessity every available person is a farmer, most of the energy controlled by humans is stored in food and feed. These are complex molecules synthesized by plants at a very low efficiency of energy utilization, and the release of energy from such molecules entails much further waste. When the United States first became a republic, human labor inefficiently furnished a quarter, and the labor of animals a half, of all the energy that kept the nation and its inhabitants functioning. Today in backward countries most work is still done by using the human body as a converter of chemical into mechanical energy, with wife and bullock of nearly equal importance. Because of this, in such lands as India more than 90 percent of human labor must be spent in growing and distributing food, yet not enough can be produced for everyone. As a consequence many starve, and less than one-twentieth of all human working time can be devoted to occupations other than those involving bare subsistence. Storing energy in starches, sugars, and fats to be later released in the sweat of man's brow is expensive, inefficient, and, if overdone in a seventy-hour or more week, debilitating.

Because we now instead do most of our work with machines that take energy from simple sources, each citizen of the United States can have two thousand times as much energy working for him as would have been available had he lived in 1800. In the last fifty years, we have acquired four million farm tractors, and have gotten rid of three-fourths of our draft horses and mules, much of whose effort had to be spent in producing their own feed. A tractor or bulldozer can do the work of a dozen horses and six men, or of forty men with shovels, on energy costing less than two dollars a day. Since most laborers can now earn this amount with less than two hours of work, they can save much effort by spending money for gasoline or electric power instead of extra bread and potatoes, for hydrocarbons rather than carbohydrates. The same atoms are involved in the two kinds of molecules, but they are differently arranged. So effective is this improvement that only one-thirtieth of the energy we use now is taken from food, instead of the one-fourth of 1780. As a result our eating habits are changing greatly; each American now consumes only half as much starchy food as did his forebears in 1900.

Beneath the surf and breakers of the economic seas lie the deep-welling technological tides that control the prosperity of nations. In the United States, productivity per person has for many years been doubling each generation. Now each man, woman, and child has nearly ten horsepower working for him day and night, instead of the two of 1900, and at present the amount of energy we each use is more than doubling every twenty years. With only 7 percent of the world's population, we control almost half of its supply of power, and as a result our standard of living is seven times the average of the rest of the world.

Man's ability to convert energy efficiently from one form to another continues to increase rapidly. Forty years ago one kilowatt hour of electrical energy could be obtained from about 3.5 pounds of coal; today only one pound is needed, and 12 ounces will soon be enough. Unfortunately, the small gasoline engines that have been found useful to propel boats, lawn mowers, and snowplows, because they can carry their energy supply stored in a small tank, are too noisy, dirty, and uncertain to serve the housewife indoors for running her dishwasher, vacuum cleaner, or clothes-dryer. Electric motors are therefore used instead, even though they must be fed energy through connected wires. The electric motor is a great emancipator of human hands, for it is clean and quiet, can be made to exert any strength desired, is tireless, seldom needs attention, and uses no energy when at rest. Increasingly motors help to compensate the housewife for the loss of domestic servants that has resulted from the availability of better jobs in factories as the new machines of the industrial age have brought these into being.

When we buy energy we pay, not for the energy itself, but for the effort that went into gathering it and bringing it to us. One kilowatt hour of electric energy costs only a few tenths of a cent to generate with either burning coal or falling water, but it usually costs ten times as much when delivered to the home. Most of the extra charge is for transmission costs, and for the privilege of turning the power on or off at will.

Until the coming of nuclear power the cheapest way to carry energy, especially over long distances, has been to keep it locked up in molecules of coal or oil, and to carry these in a ship. Over land it is most feasible economically to pump oil or gas through a large pipe line like the Big Inch, especially when thousands of miles of travel are involved. This method is also being applied to coal, powdered and floated in water or oil. But even when the cheapest and best of these methods is used, carrying energy to the user ordinarily costs from four to ten times as much as getting it out of the ground, or scooping it from a waterfall with a hydroelectric plant.

The age of nuclear power will bring great savings in

energy transport, for a pound of uranium carries more releasable energy than 1500 tons of coal. When the needed new methods of conversion have been better developed, energy transfer costs to the power station should become negligible, and power plants to feed big cities should become emancipated from the necessity of being located near the seacoast, or near coal mines, waterfalls, or dam sites.

2

All of the energy we use, except "atomic energy," has come to us from the sun. Three-fourths of it came to earth ages ago, and was stored first in the leaf cells of plants, and later in coal, oil, and gas deposits, which we now are depleting rapidly. The other fourth, including water power and the energy stored in the molecules of foodstuffs, made its eight-minute journey from the sun only recently. This glowing globe sends us more than twenty thousand times as much energy as we use now for every purpose. In fact, the earth absorbs in sunlight each day as much energy as would be released by two million atomic bombs of the Hiroshima variety. Unfortunately scientists don't yet know how to capture and store this energy effectively enough to make it worth using in large quantities, except after intermediate concentration and storage by nature in plants and in the clouds. Both of these processes waste much more energy than they concentrate.

All of the energy the earth gets from the sun eventually serves to keep the world warm, but this energy can be used for many purposes first and later will keep the world warm anyway, just as water, after dancing in a fountain, can be piped off to keep a garden green. Neither energy nor matter are ever "used up"; they are only converted and modified until they escape out of the reach of mankind into the basic reservoirs of the universe.

We use energy in three principal ways. In America, roughly a third is used to help control the environment by heating homes and factories, another third serves to process matter in mining and industry, and the remainder is spent in moving ourselves and our possessions from place to place in ships, airplanes, autos, trains, and streetcars.

Until 1880, most of the energy used by man came from burning wood, which was replaceable as fast as trees would grow. Since then we have relied increasingly on irreplaceable coal, oil, and gas, whose great value lies in the concentrated form of the energy they hold, and the ease with which this can be released simply by combining their molecules with oxygen. The energy in a pound of gasoline is sufficient to push an auto twenty times as far as that in a pound of electric storage battery fully charged.

Seventy billion barrels of oil have already been removed from the earth's crust, and in each generation experts predict that the supply will near exhaustion by the time another generation has passed. But the main reason they can seldom see more than twenty-five years' worth of petroleum resources ahead is that the oil industry becomes less diligent in hunting for more oil when its reserves are built up to that degree. Geophysicists are still able to find oil faster than the world can burn it. Their hunting methods must constantly be made more sensitive, however, and how long they will be able to keep this up is anybody's guess. When all the oil wells do go dry, oil shale, a mixture of rock and petroleum, of which enough is in sight to keep industry going for one hundred years or so, can be processed for fuel. After this is gone, coal can be hydrogenated, though at some loss in efficiency, to form liquid fuels. In South Africa, where there are no oil wells, but where the concentration of automobiles in some cities is as great as in the United States, more than 3000 tons of coal are now being converted into oil each day by the addition of hydrogen atoms to its carbon.

Though the coal in sight may last the world for a thousand years, for a long time less coal has been mined per year in America than was mined in 1910. The coal industry needs a heavy dose of technological salts to bring it back to its proper position as a leading supplier of packaged energy. Coal is harder to get out of the ground and to transport than oil, and it leaves ash. These limitations may well be removed by burning, powdering, or fluidizing coal at the mine, and then piping the resulting products to places where they are needed.

Water power appeals to engineers as being clean and readily convertible into electric energy, and is continually replenished as the sun's heat evaporates water that falls again as rain. It is not cheap to collect, however, and only 5 percent of the energy used in the United States now comes from this source. If all the potential dam sites were developed, the resulting power would fill only one-fourth of our present needs. Yet much more can be done to make hydroelectric power available. In such countries as India, powerfull hydroelectric sites lie undisturbed, while peasants cook their one hot meal a day on burning dung from holy cows.

Despite the advantages of oil and coal, more wood is cut for fuel today in the world than ever before. In Brazil, for example, 85 percent of all the energy used still comes from wood. However, in most forward-looking countries wood is becoming more valuable for the matter it contains than as a source of energy. All the cellulose our forests can produce will soon be needed for lumber and paper, and to furnish cellulose molecules for making rayon and other fibers. By 2000 A.D., less than forty-five years away, our forests should be routinely tidied up to serve as factories that use the energy of sunlight to make complex molecules out of simple carbon dioxide and water from the air.

There are several vast sources of energy that we do not now find it worthwhile to tap. An ordinary storm that covers several states develops several hundred billion horsepower, and inventors have always dreamed of using the energy of the winds. Even a minor hurricane releases energy as fast as a thousand atomic bombs exploded each second. But this power is hard to harness, and an industrial source of energy must be dependable, and not too variable in output. To be effective as a power converter, a windmill must be very large. Calculations show a good diameter to be over 200 feet, topping a twenty-story building, and for industrial power such a windmill should give out at least 2000 kilowatts no matter how fast the air is moving. However, when a breeze doubles in speed to a brisk wind it does eight times as much work as before. A zephyr blowing at less than 20 miles an hour is too weak to give the needed power; when it rises to a hurricane wind of 100 miles an hour, it can do one hundred and twenty-five times as much work, but is likely to blow the windmill away. So instead of using the wind for power we use power to make wind, as with electric fans and airplane propellers.

Much energy is stored in the oceans, not only in waves and in the tides, but as temperature differences between the warm surface and cooler depths. However, up to now the great size of the installations needed, and losses from storms, have kept methods for collecting energy from the first two from being successful. Attempts to take energy from the tides, which might well succeed in places where a great head of water rushes in and out at every tidal flow and ebb, as in the Bay of Fundy, have run up against economic difficulties, usually because such locations are not near enough to cities that could use the power without high transmission costs.

Recently we have become increasingly aware of two great

sources of energy that appear inexhaustible, the sun and the nuclei of atoms. Will solar or nuclear power run the industries of the future? The answer is both, plus all the energy sources we exploit at present. Energy is so important to man that his need for it is endless; he uses every new source to supplement rather than to supplant his older supplies.

3

The matter in an atom is all energy, as Einstein indicated in 1905 with his famous formula $E = mc^2$, in which E represents energy, m quantity of matter, and c the velocity of light. Scientists have now learned to release about one-thousandth of this energy by the process of nuclear fission, and as much as a hundredth by nuclear fusion. Even these small fractions are millions of times greater than those released in ordinary chemical combustion, which taps only the external reaches of the atom.

In a nuclear chain reaction, explosion of a complex and unstable nucleus, such as that of uranium, releases neutrons which, when slowed down by colliding with other atoms (such as carbon or deuterium) used as "moderators," react with the nuclei of neighboring explosive atoms to cause them to rearrange into new patterns and release still further showers of neutrons. A pound of U 235, the isotope of uranium which when separated from ordinary uranium was first found able to support a nuclear chain reaction, can thus be made to release as much energy as three million pounds of coal gives when burned. Only one atom out of 139 of mined uranium consists of this isotope, however. This scarcity is offset by the fact that U 238, the plentiful isotope, can be converted into plutonium atoms by bombarding its atoms with neutrons, and the newly produced atoms can then be used as nuclear fuel. The development of the breeder pile, which uses this reaction, has greatly increased our visible energy stores. The operator of a breeder pile is somewhat in the position of a householder who shovels coal and ashes into his furnace, heats his house adequately, and then shovels out, instead of ashes, tons of coke that he can sell to the neighbors.

If it were not for the dangerous radiations produced by its activity, a nuclear reactor could be rather light. As it is, heavy shields are needed to protect its operators from radiations which, besides being directly damaging to living cells, produce lethal rays when they strike sand or air or any other surrounding material. Nearby innocuous atoms will, on being struck by a ray, be converted into unstable atoms, many of which are likely to explode and emit more rays at some future time. The automobiles powered by "pea-sized plutonium engines" predicted by some journalists have lost much of their appeal because of the necessity of placing a concrete shield several feet thick under the driver's seat, and heavy concrete fenders to protect the passers-by.

Because of the dangers of contamination from waste products that might escape after an accident, any nuclear reactor must be carefully supervised in its operation. This dampens our enthusiasm for nuclear-driven locomotives. Mopping up contaminated wreckage is a tedious and, if care is not taken, a dangerous job.

Literally hundreds of different types of nuclear reactors have been designed, and these will soon evolve into as great variety as have ordinary engine-driven vehicles, which are differentiating into a thousand forms, from tractors to helicopters. Airplanes driven by nuclear power seem practicable if the shielding problem for personnel can be solved, as by putting the power plant in a tractor plane and the pilots and passengers into one or more gliders, far enough behind to escape dangerous rays. Ships are already being driven by nuclear power, though their ability to carry enough stored energy to propel them as long as they can hold together will be limited by the need for occasionally sifting out nuclear ash from the fuel. Nuclear fuel can already compete in cost with oil for driving ships, but the first cost of a nuclear power plant is still much greater than that of an oil-burning station.

Reactors to produce electric power from nuclear fuels are now being built both here and abroad, and some soon to be designed should give enough power to fill the needs of the largest city. All of the electrical power now used in the United States could be produced in theory by converting 60 tons of uranium. Though nuclear fuel lasts for many years, it needs repurification occasionally when it becomes too full of spent nuclei. Reactors for producing electric power now being built in England are expected to save 20 million tons of coal a year.

Nuclear power can already compete with domestic power costs for fuel and upkeep where these are above two cents a kilowatt hour wholesale, but the first cost and carrying charges are still too high. In Europe, where anything approaching a cent per kilowatt hour can compete, uranium is already within a factor of two to three of being a commercial success as a fuel for power. Though it is unlikely to put the coal or oil industries out of business, it should by 1975 compete with them strongly in large power operations, especially in areas far from marine transportation.

There is a great deal of uranium in the world. Some living cells tend to concentrate it, and it is likely to be found with coal. Though sea water contains only 2.5 parts per billion of uranium, the granite of the eternal hills carries about four parts in a million of uranium and 12 of thorium, and any ton of granite could give the energy of 50 tons of coal once its content of these atoms was separated out.

A few years ago, when only uranium atoms of the U 235 isotope seemed fit for industrial energy release, the nuclear fuel in sight was equivalent to about 600 billion tons of coal, or one-sixth of the world's reserves of fuel. The breeder pile, however, has raised visible nuclear energy reserves to the equivalent of 90 trillion tons of coal, and our visible energy store of all kinds is increased perhaps twenty-five-fold over what could be seen a few years ago. Thus man has been given extra ability either to destroy himself, or to carry his development further to unimagined heights.

4

Basking in the sunshine on a bright June day, we are not likely to think of our sun as the stabilized hydrogen reactor that it is. If all the light and heat radiated by this smaller than average star were focused on the earth, it would vaporize the oceans and shrivel our planet in a matter of seconds. At the center of the sun, at temperatures like those in the center of an A-bomb, the nuclei of hydrogen atoms fuse into helium nuclei, thus converting about one percent of the matter in each nucleus into energy. Fortunately we receive only two-billionths of this energy, just enough to keep the earth comfortably warm.

The sunlight that falls on a single acre of the welcoming earth contains enough energy to keep a thousand people healthy, active, and comfortable. Instead most of it is wasted, and the remainder serves on the average only one or two persons. A 16-mile-square area in any desert receives enough sunshine to satisfy all the energy needs of the American people today. Someone has calculated that the sun gives

the earth every three days as much energy as would be released by burning all the forests, and all the coal and oil and
gas in the world.

Thus we receive a large supply of solar energy, and it
appears to be free to anyone who wishes to scoop it up.
But anyone who tries is likely to become disheartened by
the many ways in which sunshine eludes his grasp, and is
missing when he needs it most. The sun is overhead only
part of the time. To light a city at night, the energy must
be held for several hours. To heat houses, it must be stored
for days or months. We lack a cheap and efficient method
of storing energy in quantity. In photosynthesis, on which
all life depends, nature has developed a storage system that
will hold energy for years in plant cells, but this operates at
too low an efficiency to compete with the coal and oil that
took thousands of times longer to produce than it does to
burn. Fuel alcohol from potatoes or other crops, one of the
best containers of stored solar energy, now costs four or five
times as much as gasoline to produce.

Seven thousand four hundred horsepower flow continuously into the top of the atmosphere above each acre of land
or sea facing the sun, but absorption and scattering by the
molecules of the air, and the inclination of the earth's axis,
in the latitude of New York reduce this to less than 4000
horsepower by the time it reaches the ground. Cloudy
weather cuts it further to a yearly average of about 800
horsepower per acre. This is still a great deal of energy, but
unfortunately storing it, carrying it to where it is to be used,
and transforming it into the chemical, electrical, mechanical,
and thermal forms we want for industry, are likely to waste
more than 85 percent of the remainder, or to require setting
up installations which are too expensive to be practical. Some
of the losses arise from immutable laws of nature, but others
can be avoided by ingenuity and scientific acumen, and
therein lies great hope for the future.

All of the many methods of catching sunlight suggested thus far have been found to be too complicated, too inefficient, or too expensive to be practical. Most new-fledged solar-energy hunters are smitten with the idea of concentrating sunlight with mirrors. A horsepower per square yard looks very attractive as an inflow of power. Let's put up a reflector ten yards on a side and concentrate 100 horsepower to run a steam engine! But large mirrors are costly and fragile, must be kept clean and free of dust, and must be turned to hold the sun's image still as the earth rotates. A boiler with all the needed gadgets and a mirror large enough to produce only two horsepower on a sunny day costs about one thousand dollars.

In India, a government scientific agency has put on the market, at fourteen dollars, a simple solar-operated cookstove. This has a mirror about one yard square which concentrates energy on a pressure cooker. The cook need only move the mirror or the pot occasionally to keep the sun's image on it. Using this device may result in saving for fertilizer much of the cow dung now used for fuel, but if enough of this can be saved to fertilize eucalyptus trees effectively, it may be found cheaper in the long run to let the trees store solar energy, and then burn their wood for cooking.

The trouble with large installations for solar power is that they cost too much to build and to keep up. The solar energy falling on a square mile in a day is worth two hundred thousand dollars at present power rates. At 5 percent efficiency of conversion this would give a daily income of ten thousand dollars. However, any apparatus yet suggested to capture and convert this much energy would cost millions of dollars a square mile, and the interest on this amount would be more than ten thousand dollars a day. Keeping the glass or mirrors used shiny and in repair would also be expensive. Yet if scientists can even double present efficiencies, solar energy capture may go from the economic red into the black.

There is some hope that better methods of conversion can be found, especially those like the thermopile and the photovoltaic cell, which convert solar radiation directly into electrical power. Greatly encouraging was the announcement in 1953 by scientists of the Bell Telephone Laboratories that a new cell made of thin strips of specially treated silicon gave about 50 watts per square yard when exposed to sunlight. This efficiency of 4 percent has since been increased to more than 10 percent. Though such solar batteries are not likely to be used as an industrial source of power until they can be made more cheaply, in this direction lies much hope.

We may be on the verge of using solar energy far more widely for heating our homes and hot water for domestic use. Solar houses have been operated through the winter even in New England with only 10 percent addition of furnace heat. For such applications sunlight need not be concentrated, but can be allowed to fall directly on blackened metal absorbers on a house roof, tilted at the best angle to soak up heat during the winter months. These boxes must be well insulated, and covered with one or more layers of very clear glass to act as a heat trap, like a greenhouse. A nonfreezing water solution is circulated under the blackened surface of the collector, and carries the heat to an insulated storage bin, and thence as needed to radiators. Such collectors now cost about two dollars a square foot; if their cost could be cut in half, solar heating would become very attractive, and larger installations to generate power from solar energy might become economically feasible.

As many as 20 tons of water, gravel, or a solution of chemical salts is needed to store enough energy to heat a house for a single day, which requires that at least 5 percent of the useful space of the building must be devoted to insulated heat storage bins. But if at least a ten-day supply of energy cannot be counted on, central heating must be provided for stand-by use in cold and cloudy weather. This doubles the cost of a solar house-heating plant. This extra expense may be justified if the stand-by heater is of the heat-pump type, which can be used also for cooling in summer, or even if electric air-conditioning and heating are used.

Nature's solution of the solar energy storage problem, photosynthesis in the cells of plants, though very inefficient, is effective, for it stores energy in chemical form where it will stay indefinitely in the elastic insides of molecules. It has been suggested that furnaces could be run on algae or other simple plants grown for fuel. This would be a ridiculous waste of effort, involving building up at great expense very complicated molecules to do a job that much simpler molecules could do more effectively. Stoking stoves with starch or sugar is as silly as it sounds.

Energy from the sun, though it comes from the nuclei of atoms, by the time it reaches the earth has been made diffuse enough to be safely fed to the delicate complex molecules from which plants and later animals are formed. When nuclear energy is released on earth, it is concentrated and intense, and to gentle it we must control great quantities of dangerous rays. It is natural then for the scientist to plan to use nuclear energy in those cases where he must have high temperatures, pressures, and energy concentrations, and to use solar energy where gentle diffuse actions are required. For the ordinary purposes of industry, solar energy needs concentrating, while nuclear energy needs diffusing. At the moment, scientists are getting on faster with the latter, but both will have great importance in man's future.

5

What is this thing called energy, which man can use for his destruction, or to set himself ever freer from control by his environment? We recognize it in many forms, as light or heat or sound or electric power, but all have in common the capacity for doing work. They are merely different external manifestations of three basic forms that exist in the realm of protons, neutrons, and electrons: energy resulting from electrical, magnetic, and gravitational forces.

The deeper we dig into the structure of matter, the greater the amounts of releasable energy we find. The events of the world we contact with our senses are only leftovers, which result from residual forces not balanced out on the fundamental levels of matter. We have seen that protons combine with neutrons in the nucleus with forces measured in millions of volts. Forces corresponding to a few thousands of volts remain unbalanced, and with these the nucleus collects a family of electrons to form an atom. With still smaller residual forces, from a dozen volts down, these atoms cluster into molecules and crystals. It is the rest of this residue of a remainder, measured in thousandths of a volt for each material, that determines whether these molecules shall form shoes or ships or sealing wax.

The flowing of a waterfall, the heating of a house, and the hitting of an enemy with a club utilize only minor routine residues of energy. With the coming of the Industrial Age men learned how to bring the energy of the molecular world, through chemical reactions, directly to bear on mechanical problems, at the same time learning better how to harness the older residual forms of energy. With gunpowder, and later gasoline, they were able to release energy in much more concentrated form and in greater quantity. In the early years of this century scientists sensed the even more concentrated and vaster supply of energy in the nucleus of the atom, and in 1942 they learned how to release this energy directly.

Unfortunately, "atomic" energy from the nucleus is being born to mankind with its least attractive features first visible, and looks to many frightened laymen like an evil thing well left alone. However, the destructive applications, of which we are at present rightly but inordinately fearful, should before long take their proper position relative to far greater positive contributions to human welfare. Mastery of the nucleus will mark a much bigger step in man's ability to control his environment than any he has taken before, for it gives him the opportunity to be at home on more fundamental levels of the material world, instead of merely working in the outskirts. Calling the release of nuclear energy a "new Promethean fire" is more than just a metaphor or an analogy. The new fire of atoms presents to man an opportunity similar to that he received when he first drew back a burned finger from the fire of molecules, now raised in intensity to a transcendent power.

When nuclear fission occurs, as we have said only about one-thousandth of the energy content of an atom is released, and scientists know how to set this energy free from only a few of the heavier kinds of natural atoms. But with the processes of nuclear fusion, up to ten times as much of an atom's energy can be released. In its simplest form fusion involves the combination of two protons with two neutrons to form the nucleus of a helium atom. The sun gets most of its energy in this way, and most matter in the universe is probably thus formed as a first step. Though the sun is an excellent hydrogen fusion reactor, it is early yet to decide whether we can ever have on earth a small one so well controlled, one that will operate at a strong simmer instead of exploding in a millionth of a second, or that must be kept a thousand miles away to be of use. If the speed, instead of merely the extent, of a thermonuclear reaction can ever be controlled, water may well furnish a super-fuel better than any of those of which men have dreamed.

Inventors who have tried to develop pills that would make

water burn were on the wrong track, for water is already ashes of hydrogen. When hydrogen is burned with oxygen their molecules combine to produce water, and release much chemical energy in the flame. The water remains after the energy is dissipated, and new energy must be used to "un-burn" the water as plants do in photosynthesis, or as electric power can be made to do in a hydrogen generator. But if protons are collected from the hydrogen in water and then assembled with neutrons to produce helium nuclei, a vastly greater release of energy results, energy from nearer the base of universal supply. At present no one appears to know how to control this reaction beyond setting it off with an atomic bomb as a primer, thus raising nuclear temperatures to those needed to start a fusion reaction. If this process could be slowed down and controlled, the oceans would provide an inexhaustible reservoir of energy, and man need never worry about power again. But he has much to learn before this can come about.

Of equal importance to man's rapidly improving ability to control energy of the most intense forms, like that of the multibillion volt cosmic rays, is his increasing mastery of the most subtle forces, those that hold atoms together in complex living molecules. When these forces can be better controlled the physical hungers of all humanity can be filled by further gentling of the energies of the atom bomb into those of food and warmth. Then will it become apparent that energy from the atom, far from being the evil creation of a few clever but dangerous men, is a beneficent force of nature that has been lying in wait since the beginning of time, until man could awaken to awareness of its availability, and learn properly to control it.

Chapter Four

The Coming to Life

What does it mean to be alive? We feel that we know, because we *are* alive, but to decide whether some specific piece of matter contains life or not is far from simple. We who have seen living creatures die are likely to think of three categories of aliveness: one that includes machines, minerals, and other things that have never been alive; one containing such creatures as cabbages and kings that live; and one of dead kings and cabbages that live no longer. This turns out to be much too simple a picture.

There are millions of levels of being alive. Certainly the basic electrons, protons, and neutrons of matter, though they move and are full of energy, and though all living things are composed of them, are themselves inanimate. So are the atoms formed from them. The level on which life begins seems to be the next higher, that of the molecule. But the more closely one examines the borderline between living and nonliving matter, the more is one forced to conclude that there is no boundary that is definite, no place where a breath of life comes sharply to inform matter. Yet we have a good criterion of aliveness: matter that is animate has a certain special ability to increase the organization of almost any amount of other matter of specific types with which it comes in contact, to arrange atoms into new and special molecules.

Matter that exists in patterns that have had a certain amount of what might be called "evolutionary experience" has the ability to put these in turn into ever greater elaborations of cells and organisms and societies.

The properties of living matter seem so different from those of matter that is not alive, and its organized complexity so much greater, that some of us find difficulty in conceiving the phenomenon of life as existing without a constantly supervising internal Force. Others find it quite as natural to suppose an initial Plan, in which the potentiality of every creature to come is built into the properties of the primordial particles. It is neither materialistic nor irreverent to ask for evidence of either of these devices, and to seek enlightenment by looking at the majestic and awe-inspiring panorama of Creative Evolution. There we see that the God that made the sparrow certainly made the proton first.

Every human body originates as a fertilized egg cell so small as to be barely visible, half a hundredth of an inch across. A cup would hold the cells from which all the 164 million people now living in the United States got their start. Within this partial pint of matter, nine-tenths of it water, are apparently contained complete directions for assembling atoms not only to form the bodies of all these people, but also those of their billions of descendants for countless generations. What determines that one small cell is to develop into a sweet girl with blue eyes and fair hair; that another, obtained elsewhere but looking somewhat similar, will become a butterfly; and another a sponge? We need not, unless we wish, suppose a pattern hidden in some inner world to be guiding the formation and laying down of each atom in a molecule, each molecule in a living cell, each cell in an organ, each organ in a body. The potentialities of the most complex of God's creatures appear to be built into the basic particles of matter themselves.

To make this plausible requires a mechanism for storing vast amounts of information in a tiny cell. The arrangement of the atoms in a living molecule seems to serve this purpose. Though a cell is microscopic, the molecules of which it is composed are far smaller. In fact, there are more molecules in a cell than there are cells in a man, and this latter number, about twenty-five million million, is itself ten thousand times as large as the number of people now living in the world.

In the structures of molecules that carry life, nature gives very express directions as to the further organization of the cells that are to be built around them—these are to form a tooth of such a shape and hardness, these a lung, these eyes with hazel irises, these hair without a curl—all in terms of trillions of yeses and noes arranged in the hereditary genes, the molecular pattern-holders. Though a gene is only a molecule, someone has computed that the amount of information that can be stored in the various arrangements of its many thousands of atoms is far greater than that contained in the words of a thousand volumes of encyclopedias. To visualize this we must go back to the beginnings of life.

It has been calculated that less than one-billionth of the matter of our world is alive, in the sense of being incorporated into living creatures. This life has developed during the more recent half of the earth's four or five billion years of existence as a world. Primitive lichens, which had already learned to use energy from the sun to build up complex molecules, are found in fossil beds measured as two thousand million years old by radioactive dating methods. But these certainly do not represent the earliest life, for they were land plants, and they were made of cells, and these developed only long after the beginnings of organic evolution. The earth was already two thousand, five hundred million years old when these lichens existed, and its rocky face was much as we know it now. Such old continents as Australia had been around for a billion years. Presumably life had started much earlier in the sea, which at that time contained a fine concentrated soup of nourishing molecules of moderate size, which enabled increasingly large molecules to become stable.

The basis of life is now believed by many biologists to be a molecule which, in the proper environment, can attract atoms and arrange them in such a way as to build a replica of itself. Of this the molecules called genes are the best examples. A tiny corkscrew, dipped into molten metal for a moment, might be pictured as bringing out a tin duplicate of itself, which would peel off on cooling and could be used to make another corkscrew by dipping. Admittedly all conditions would have to be just right to keep from melting the corkscrew each time, but so must it be also with living molecules.

As we have seen, the Second Law of Thermodynamics tells how to measure the degree of organization of matter, to see how far a given object departs from the chaos which its atoms would approach if left alone. Playing cards tossed in the air seldom sort themselves into suits, but tend to fall at random. Atoms behave similarly. A turnip is an ordered assembly of atoms, which needs the touch of life held by its genes to produce this order.

The whole universe is tending to run down, says the Second Law, with hot suns getting colder and the clockwork of the universe gradually slowing. In the midst of this degeneration appears the directing force called Life. By organization this creates a narrow pinnacle of co-operative achievement rising in the midst of gathering chaos. It is as if nature had been given, through evolution, the task of trying to build creatures to the stature of the gods so that they could get a hand-hold on Valhalla before the scaffold falls away, when the present manifestation of our universe grows cold.

The life principle of organization may well have appeared first on earth, then, in large self-duplicating molecules that were able to remain stable in certain chemical surroundings because of special properties possessed by the carbon atom. All living molecules are found to be built around this atom. By arranging carbon and hydrogen atoms in patterns, with oxygen and nitrogen atoms placed in strategic positions, and with an occasional sulfur or phosphorous atom tied in here and there, large molecules containing up to several hundred thousand atoms can be formed. No other atom than carbon has the fine symmetry that gives the power to hold such large molecules together. These, the bricks from which all living things are made, are called proteins, as being basic or primary to life.

A molecule containing one hundred thousand atoms is as complex, in its way, as a city containing one hundred thousand people. Even though the atoms in a protein molecule may be of only five or six kinds, when there are thousands of them they can be arranged in an unbelievable number of combinations, each producing a different result. Such big molecules have sub-parts as a large city has boroughs; among the most important parts of the proteins are the amino-acids. These are sub-molecules of which nearly two dozen kinds are known, which furnish most of the structural material for the animal world.

To build up a large protein molecule, assemble a group of amino-acid molecules after snipping off a water molecule from the end of each, and string them into groups called peptide chains. Their ends will snap together to form strong hinged joints, held by forces between a nitrogen atom on one and a carbon and oxygen pair on the other. From the central chain of such a molecule hundreds of amino-acid side chains can be strung in various arrangements, like ribs along a backbone. The resulting peptide chains are likely to curl

up into helices, and these helices to group together into
bundles, then into fibers, sheets, and balls. From these nature
has learned by repeated trial to build increasingly complex
animated mechanisms, or, as some prefer, vehicles of animation.

To carry out such an assembling process, nature uses foremen molecules called enzymes. These are special proteins
which, though not able to duplicate themselves, can nevertheless facilitate the assembling of atoms into molecules of needed
forms by aiding certain chemical reactions and suppressing
others. Enzymes are in the molecular world like the jigs or
templates that a carpenter uses to assemble a large number of
similar window frames or other objects. The enzyme molecules are not used up in the process, but act as structural
forms. They are matchmakers for atoms, speeding up, often
by as much as a millionfold, their getting together into some
special complex molecule. Certain enzymes help tear molecules apart, ripping them at selected seams so that the resulting useful atomic groups can be fitted into other molecular forms. Wherever life is found we observe that all the
chemical processes are under the control of enzymes. Bacteria produce many enzymes that carry on the multitudinous
operations of microbiology, and control many fermentation
and digestion processes of great importance to higher animals.

Thus the coming of life is seen to be a gradual thing, one
new ability at a time being developed as the organization of
matter into more complex groupings is achieved. Once a
molecule had gained the marvelous ability to reproduce itself,
we say it was alive, but it could not move at will, or feel or
think or yearn. It had a long way to go to learn to behave
properly as part of even an amoeba, and beyond that aeons
were required to develop for it an improved environment in
a sponge, a turtle, a robin, or a man. But it was on the way.

2

Lowest in the scale of life appear to be certain viruses, naked nucleo-protein molecules on the borderline between the inanimate and the living. Some, like tobacco mosaic virus, form readily into crystals, as do inanimate molecules, yet they multiply as parasites of cells and show the organizing ability of living creatures. Viruses attack both plant and animal cells, and live on their contents. Some are responsible for well-known diseases of man, such as smallpox, scarlet fever, measles, and poliomyelitis. Others, called bacteriophage, attack the single-celled bacteria which cause other diseases, so we consider them friendly to man. Viruses range in size from giants containing a number of molecules, only slightly smaller than bacteria, down to those that produce yellow fever, which consist of a few thousand atoms arranged like a cigar only a millionth of an inch thick.

Experiments using as tracers exploding atoms such as radioactive phosphorus, have shown that a typical virus consists of a very large protein molecule to which is attached one or more molecules of nucleic acid, a basic material of life found in the nuclei of all cells. Each of these viruses has on its surface, like a molecular drill, an active area of enzyme that can dissolve a part of the wall of a cell so the virus can break into it. In one case in which such a virus, a bacteriophage, was observed under the microscope to enter a single-celled bacterium, the cell after twenty-four minutes swelled up and two hundred new viruses exactly like the first came popping out, while the cell collapsed like an emptied sack.

Genes, which appear to many geneticists to be the real masters of the living world, are of a slightly higher order of life than viruses, for they have learned to gather in groups called chromosomes, and to build a chemical stockade, a cell wall, around their colony. The naked viruses need complex molecules to live on just as the genes do, but don't go to the trouble of synthesizing these, living instead on the provender stored in cells by their genes. Viruses may represent degenerate types of genes, or even a more elementary way station on the path of evolution.

When genes had gradually learned the advantages of cooperation and finally invented the cell, many new possibilities opened up. Groups of molecules could do many things that single ones could not, no matter how large a molecule might grow. They were able to surround themselves with a jelly of protoplasm containing all sorts of complex molecules, including enzymes, held together within a cell wall stiffened with a plaster of calcium atoms, and so could build a protection against the chemically cruel outer world. Ultimately they apparently became so expert at forming and directing their cells that it is natural now for us to think of life in terms of the cells themselves as units, instead of the genes that they enclose. Many creatures, both plant and animal, today still consist of only one such cell.

Every type of cell known, whether a single-celled creature or a part of one of the many-celled organisms developed by nature later, is held in a membrane wall, which in an oversimplified picture appears something like a tiny cellophane bag that allows certain kinds of molecules to pass through easily and keeps out others. This bag is full of jelly-like but very active protoplasm in which float the chromosomes as diffuse strings of beadlike genes. When the growing cell reaches a certain size, the chromosomes sharpen up and split as each gene duplicates itself, the cell begins to pinch through the middle, and one set of genes goes to each side of the constriction. Finally the cell divides into two new ones, each like the original. Later these two divide, and the process is repeated again and again. A single bacterium, a plant cell that divides every twenty minutes or so when in water containing the right nutrients, may thus give rise to millions of similar descendent cells within a single day.

Amoebas are single-celled animals which are relatively slow to divide, producing a new generation only every hour or so. Yet a single microscopic amoeba so dividing could in theory produce a million amoebas within twenty hours, a pound of them in twenty-nine hours, and in just under a week, if enough nourishment were available, a pile of amoebas larger than the earth. Obviously most amoebas are consumed by higher organisms, or dry up and blow away before they can divide further. The genes that inhabit them, though better off than naked viruses, need a still better means of controlling their environment.

Over the ages some types of cell found it good not to separate completely, but to meet life together in groups. There were decided advantages in forming cell societies, and all higher plants and animals are such colonies of gene-city establishments. Certain types of sponge can still be shredded into their constituent cells by forcing them through a sieve of fine mesh; if the resulting soup of cells is immersed in sea water, the cells will after a time gather together again into a new sponge and form a perfect animal.

Gradually such groups of cell colonies learned to specialize. From them plants and animals with various organs were developed, containing muscle and nerve and bone and blood and liver cells. All of these are still formed in each higher organism from the one cell that starts it off, the fertilized egg. In return for the protective environment of the colony as a whole, and for services rendered by the other cells, each cell gives up a certain amount of its freedom and loses much of its original flexibility, taking on new specialized abilities with which it can contribute more to the group. Thus muscle cells learn to expand and contract better than can the cell which is an amoeba; nerve cells learn better to stimulate their neighbors to pass on electrochemical signals; red blood cells learn to leave their nuclei behind in the bone marrow where they were born, and act as tiny barges to carry oxygen; gland cells learn to manufacture the special molecules called enzymes and hormones; bone cells get more rigid, skin cells more platelike and protective.

The body of a six-foot man contains twenty-five trillion cells, each with about thirty thousand genes in it gathered into chromosomes. From the standpoint of the man the genes are his units of heredity; from the standpoint of a gene it lives in a co-operative commonwealth. It and its fellows have organized chromosomes and established cell-states; these cells again have learned to co-operate and to specialize, and have formed an organic nation.

Thus we see from the record of evolution that coming alive is a slow process, and must be learned in steps. Each new entity has the job of working things out, of showing what it can do in the environment where it has developed. Entirely new aspects of being alive are enlarged by each successful new entity. New degrees of aliveness are being created on earth faster now than ever before, as the Tree of Life proliferates ever further.

3

All creatures, in their development from a single cell to maturity, pass rapidly through the forms of even their remote ancestors. Each human embryo shows the gill arches of the fish; every unborn whale has legs. How does nature manage to do in a few hours or months a job that took millions of years the first time? This recapitulation becomes understandable if we take the viewpoint of a gene. Though one gene is not responsible for shaping the whole cell colony which is to become, say, the body of a man, but with others influences mainly the shape of an eyelid, the color of an iris, or the molecular output of a gland, with his thirty thousand or so companion genes he shapes the man by guiding atoms into place. This the genes do easily and automatically as a result of the arrangement of their own atoms, by attracting into their fields of force other atoms which undirected would form but ash and air. But they are all successful genes; genes incapable of such performance have quickly passed away, as the creatures they produced and which carried them were found unable to withstand the tests of living. Aeons were needed in evolution, not for building organisms the first time, but for forming and trying genes by the trillions until the right ones were developed. When they are at hand each can do its entire job as fast as the needed atoms can be snapped into place.

Changing a single gene, only millionths of an inch on a side, yet containing thousands of atoms, can cause a fly that normally has two wings to develop into one with four, or make a man have club feet. The number of such genes in a chromosome, and of chromosomes in a cell, depends on the kind of plant or animal to which the cell belongs. Fruit flies have only four chromosomes, each with about a thousand genes; humans have twenty-four chromosomes, with a total of some thirty thousand genes, in each cell. Biologists can watch through the microscope while cells divide, and see each chromosome split to carry duplicate genes into the new cells. Not only do the genes in these chromosomes carry the information that is to arrange identical atoms into a carrot, a bee, or a man, but they have the power to start the wheels turning to assemble the raw molecules that are drawn into each cell.

Though the material in a cell looks liquid, it is on the

verge of becoming solid at any instant, with its molecules poised to snap into fixed positions at the proper chemical signal. Probably each gene controls an enzyme; like a punched card controlling a machine, it directs the synthesis of the proper enzymes to control the workings of the cell. The enzymes in an egg cell are prevented by some chemical mechanism from starting their work of sorting atoms and assembling molecules until fertilization takes place. The cell is coated with a chemical layer that keeps out other cells, but a sperm cell of the same species carries the proper enzyme key. Once this key is used the lock is plugged, and the cell begins to divide. By the time a baby chick is ready to peck its way out of the shell a few weeks after the cell division starts, its stomach wall alone contains more than ten million cells.

Even more remarkable than the ability of nature to develop genes that direct atoms into patterns which increasingly fit the environment, is the ability of the genes to keep the same patterns over millions of duplications of themselves. Individual genes are certainly not immortal, and their matter is in constant flux. Though atoms may last for billions of years, trading their external electrons fairly frequently and nuclear particles on occasion, tracer experiments with exploding atoms show that the molecules and cells of our bodies are constantly being reconstituted. Most of the cells in a human body are replaced oftener than once in two years, and their atoms are exchanged even more frequently. Cells have little permanence of substance, but great continuity of form, like the flame of a candle.

This being so, it is a miracle of life that genes like those that produce the colony of cells we call an opossum could keep this pattern the same for eighty million years, or others hold the pattern of a lichen for a billion years. Since the first modern lichen was formed, many of the genes in its cells have duplicated themselves millions of times without observable change.

This stability has been explained on the basis of the Quantum Theory of matter and energy, in which atoms and molecules remain entirely unaffected by collisions with particles or rays involving less than a definite amount of energy. A world cool enough to support life involves only infrequently collisions having energy greater than that of an electron falling through 30 volts. But when a more violent collision comes, as when a cosmic ray hits a gene squarely on the nucleus of one of its atoms, a change may be produced in the qualities the gene confers. Such mutations, changes not sufficiently severe to keep the molecule from still acting as a gene yet changing the patterns it will pass along, can also be produced by heat and by strong chemicals such as mustard gas. But especially are they produced by cosmic rays and other energetic radiations that can knock electrons out of atoms and hence shift chemical bonds.

Most mutations are bad; the new gene has lost some of the abilities of the old one as a good pattern for survival, and usually has nothing better to offer. But once in a thousand times or so the new gene produces a fitter creature than the old one. This new entity nature tries out in her great laboratory of life, to compete and co-operate with other forms, according to its ability to fit or modify its environment. It then perpetuates its species in accordance with the degree of success it attains as a living creature.

Radiations from atomic bombs, apart from their direct effects on human beings, are extremely likely to produce undesirable mutations in many of the genes they strike. No human being can lightly afford to have any of his good genes changed. Though one mutation in a thousand may result in an improvement, there is no way to eliminate the undesirable ones except by the selective processes of nature over many

generations. Man, concerned as much with the individual as
with the race, almost certainly cannot afford to expose his
genes to nuclear radiations at random.

Though the genes appear in many cases to control specific body characteristics, they do not affect the individual
independently, but rather in groups. The offspring of a
single parent will be exactly like him, except as changes are
slowly accumulated over the ages by successive mutations.
A cutting from a Baldwin apple tree grows into a tree that
produces Baldwin apples. If such reproduction were the
only type available, evolutionary progress would be slowed
many millionfold. To speed it up by providing much more
diversity, nature has made use of the device called sex. This
process, the joining of two lines of inheritance by having two
members of a species each contribute half of a new set of
atomic templates, was developed very early in evolution, perhaps even before the cell was invented, for viruses show sex.
At that level of life several molecules often contribute material for a single new offspring molecule. A baby virus, if
he only knew, may have nine grandparents and many extra
uncles twice-removed.

Nature found, however, that combinations from two
strains gave all the diversity needed, and in most forms of
life settled down to two sexes. When the genes from one
cell mingle with those from another, so that each contributes
about half of the characteristics of any new individual, an
almost infinite variety of sets of characteristics results from
the myriad possible combinations of different genes. The
thirty thousand genes in each human cell control not a mere
thirty thousand characteristics, but two raised to the thirty
thousandth power, an inconceivably large number. It is estimated that more than eighty million million different gene
combinations now contribute to the human species. Since
only twenty-four hundred million humans are now alive, and

only twenty times as many have lived since the beginning of
time, more than a thousand times as many gene combinations
are available in the human stock as have ever been used.
Small wonder that no two people except identical twins ever
look alike! These, coming from an accidental early division
of a group of cells that was forming a single individual, start
as two copies of that one person. Yet all other men are
brothers too, members of a single species built from the same
stock of combining genes. But every individual differs from
every other that has lived, because no one before has ever
been organized by exactly the same set of genes.

4

The two distinct streams of evolution, plant and animal
life, can be traced back to the same living source. During
the early evolution of cells some grew lazy, and instead of
bothering to build up their own complex molecules with sunlight, they began to steal the substance of their neighbors.
Seeking complex molecules to absorb, they gradually learned
to move with purpose and became the first animals. To
escape being eaten by their co-pirates they eventually learned
to move quite rapidly. Thus single-celled animals came into
being, early prototypes of the amoeba and the paramecium.

Plants use the energy of sunlight to pull oxygen atoms, O,
out of water molecules, H_2O, and carbon, C, out of carbon
dioxide molecules, CO_2. By photosynthesis they then fashion
the complex molecules needed to build their cells and store
the energy to pump their sap. Animals get all of the energy
they need by tearing down the molecules synthesized by
plants or by other animals, recombining C and O to form CO_2
and H and O to form H_2O. Thus animals live by burning
food as fuel; plants also live by burning it for energy, but in

addition they unburn it, that is synthesize it for structural and energy storing purposes.

Though they are separate streams of life, plants and animals are mutually dependent. Some plants could remain alive if there were no animals on earth, but no animal could exist for long without plants to build up complex molecules for its use. Yet there are more plants on earth today than there would probably be if there were no animals; though some carbon would be available from the carbon dioxide produced by forest fires and other sources, including plants themselves, and especially bacteria, yeasts, and molds, that breathed out by animals makes a great addition to the stores in the atmosphere. Most plants would grow faster than they do if the air around them contained up to five times as much carbon dioxide as it does. It has been estimated that all the carbon dioxide molecules on earth are taken apart every three hundred years by the world's plants, and that all the oxygen in the atmosphere is renewed by them every twenty centuries.

Land plants manage to build 20 billion tons of carbon atoms a year into carbohydrate, fat, and protein molecules. Probably ten times as much more is synthesized by plant cells in the sea. Though land plants store energy through the agency of green chlorophyll in their leaves, it is not correct to say that most plants are green. Several other molecules than chlorophyll can be used by nature for photosynthesis, and plants that grow in the sea are usually brown.

When a fuel like wood or coal is burned in a fire, or a food like sugar is burned in an animal body, energy is set free by the releasing of figurative molecular springs that results from the rearranging of atomic partners to form CO_2 and H_2O. When carbon dioxide and water molecules are formed, the springs are almost fully collapsed. To restretch them and build up molecules packed full of energy again, plants use the photons of sunlight. To set a spring with a single push would require a larger photon than would be safe for most living molecules to absorb. Fortunately the dangerously large ultraviolet photons in sunlight are strained out by ozone at the top of the atmosphere. With this protection, nature has learned how to set the molecular energy traps by doing the job in several steps with smaller packets of radiation. A small photon, of say red light, comes along and is swallowed to cock the energy trap part way; then others are absorbed successively until the trap is entirely set. Thus the plant cell is enabled to build up big molecules from little ones.

Plants must have learned the trick of photosynthesis very early in evolution, for the building up of large molecules requires energy, and the moderate-sized molecules in the soupy sea of the earth's morning could not live entirely on each other. Those that learned to use energy from the sun to put themselves into states that attracted additional atoms got ahead fastest. Then, when gene molecules learned to develop cells as protective environments around their colonies, these became tiny molecule factories operated by sunlight. Even a very elementary type of plant life, such as a mold that grows on bread, can in a few days synthesize as many as twenty kinds of amino-acids, nine vitamins, and many even more complex molecules. The familiar green mold that synthesizes penicillin, the molecule that quickly cut in half the death rate from pneumonia, is the only plant that makes this molecule.

Single-celled plants have through gene mutations developed into many thousands of living species. The soil, the air, every body of water, and the bodies of all multi-celled animals teem with bacteria. The living world is much more dependent on these tiny plants than we realize, for they spend their lives taking apart the molecules of which larger

creatures are made, and return their atoms to forms that can
be rebuilt easily into complex molecules. Bacteria produce
many enzymes that are essential for getting food into the
proper shape for assimilation by larger creatures. Some baby
birds are even fed excrement by their parents for the first few
days after hatching, so that the right intestinal flora will start
multiplying inside them.

Long after the cell was invented, plant cells learned the
advantages of mutual co-operation and living together in
groups, and gradually evolved very complex forms of organisms. Animal cells must have made this discovery quite
independently, for the two patterns of life had diverged long
before it appeared. Like animal cells, plant cells have learned
the advantages of specialization and co-operation, developing
cells especially adapted for leaf and root and fiber. After
multi-celled plant organisms were found by nature to be useful, some plants developed strange partnerships even closer
than those of the ant and the aphid. Lichens, for example,
are composed of two separate kinds of plants, algae and fungi,
neither of which can live on barren stones without the other.
To provide basic nourishment the fungus secretes acids which
dissolve the rock on which it grows, and the alga then synthesizes from these simple molecules larger ones from which
cells for both can be formed. This process of mutual co-
operation, called symbiosis from the Greek for "living together," is seen frequently in both the plant and the animal
worlds, and indeed appears on a large scale in the mutual
dependence on each other of these two kingdoms. Each life
stream concentrates vitamins and other special molecules
needed by the other. Flowers, millions of years before they
became carriers of emotional information and a tonic for the
human spirit, were decked with color, fragrance, and nectar
as nature found it valuable to appeal to the sight, smell, and

taste of insects, so that these carriers of pollen would keep new generations of plants from remaining too provincial.

Although to a man looking at an oak tree the tree is a living entity, the genes in its billions of cells are what hold the mastery of its living form. These are the units of its life; they control its type of branching, its adaptation to moisture availability, its flowering and fruiting. More than two hundred fifty thousand different species of plants are now known, and perhaps as many more have not yet been classified.

Though successful in their way, plants have followed a course of evolution that does not give as much opportunity for environmental awareness as animals possess. These have proliferated into more than a million living species. Although the body of a tree or vine is wonderfully made, its ability to control its surroundings is limited by the fact that it is rooted to one spot, and must take whatever nourishment comes its way rather than seeking this out actively. Plants can move their branches and leaves, to be sure, but only very slowly. Their leaves turn gently toward the light; their roots swing slowly toward the proper degree of moisture; they push upward in response to tiny spirit levels in their cells. Some, such as the sensitive mimosa, whose leaves shrink quickly when touched, have even developed a sort of elementary nervous system. But most plant reactions to the environment are relatively sluggish. A lily or an onion feels no pain, for it has no pressure pickups or nerve circuits, and allows itself to be plucked or eaten without a struggle. By struggling, animals have been able to evolve into much higher forms. Building on the plant world as a base, they have been able to develop abilities far beyond those of plants, and thus to raise the scaffold of life much higher.

5

Animals have come much more alive than plants. Those that have come most alive have profited by a series of marvelous inventions made by nature over the past billion years.

After the basic invention of a cell as a co-operative venture of the genes, and that of specialization by cells to form parts of multi-celled organisms, additional developments made practicable increased sizes of cell colonies. Freer motion became possible as a result of the invention of muscles made from groups of shrinking and relaxing cells, together with carapaces and shells and bones to fasten these muscles to. Then came the various pumps. The heart gradually developed to aid in the circulation of blood, and the gills and lungs in that of oxygen. Great increases in the sizes of cell colonies became possible by the thorough aeration and nourishment of tissues that these pumps brought about, for without them the inner reaches of cells in a large body containing trillions would soon starve and rot.

Among the most successful and adaptable of living creatures are the insects, which some prophets needlessly fear may take over the world from humans. Insects account for about seven hundred thousand of the million species of animal life. Though most fish, reptiles, birds, and mammals are much larger than any insect, all of these put together would weigh less than a third as much as the insect life of the world. But the structural limitations of insects keep them from ever coming as much alive as higher animals, and they cannot develop the higher brain needed for conscious thought.

A basic limitation on the insect is that it has no lungs. A modern insect even as large as a mouse would have the same trouble human giants sometimes have with their feet, for it lacks a bellows to pull in oxygen, and blood cells to carry this to its tissues, and must rely on the natural diffusion of gases through tubes leading to each organ. Though spiders grew a foot long, and dragonflies spread 15-inch wings, in the warm and moist ages two hundred forty million years ago when palm trees grew in Greenland, today we need not fear the giant insects of the sensational journalist, for the laws of chemistry and physics make it impossible for them to stay alive in our modern atmosphere.

More than ten thousand known species of insects have developed colonies or societies, in which new levels of co-operation and specialization are reached. More than thirty-five hundred species of ants, and eighteen hundred of termites, have developed such complex organizations, some of which were going strong eighty million years ago. One termite nest in which a census was taken was found to contain nearly two million individuals, of which two hundred thousand were soldiers. The termite queen, which sometimes is more than three inches long, is fed special vitamins which turn her almost completely into a factory—she spends her dozen or so years of life looking down over her swollen abdomen, laying millions and millions of eggs.

Such social insects have developed many operations that man has later found useful. Various kinds of ants plant gardens, domesticate other insects, clear paths, carry sunshades, and specialize as nurses, soldiers, garbage collectors, or foragers. Wasps build houses of mud and of paper which they make from wood pulp; some preserve food by stinging spiders so as to paralyze but not kill them, and lay their eggs in this unwilling market of living meat. But insect societies differ from human societies in that they are governed by mass instinct rather than by emotion and reason, and the individual is completely sacrificed for the common welfare, so that he is less an organism than a mobile cell of a higher type. They are the original Communists.

The stimuli that govern ant actions are very simple. It is easy to cause a column of army ants to walk itself to death in a circle. Since the reactions of an insect society come directly from the genes, they can be changed only slowly, over the centuries, by mutations. Those of a human society can respond much more rapidly, because of the great flexibility and sublety residing in emotion and thought. Men are therefore much more alive than insects, more aware of their environment, and able to do more to change it.

Nowhere are the blessed uses of adversity better evident than in the sweeping panorama of evolution. The king crab, as we have seen, comfortable in his salty sea, has remained a crab for one hundred sixty million years. The opossum, retiring from disagreeable reality in a trance, has remained the same for eighty million years. The porcupine, fairly safe behind his quills, has never needed to become other than slow and stupid. Until the motorcar came the skunk found his evil spray a fine defense, and developed little intelligence. The armor plate of the giant lizards had the same effect on them. To survive, the mammals had to flee in fear; the faster and smarter ones got away, and their descendants lived to become men.

It is not egocentric on the part of man to consider himself the most highly evolved creature in nature. But any tendency to consider himself its end-product would be shortsighted, for evolution is taking place today faster than ever before. Physical evolution, greatly accelerated by man in the improvement of plants and animals as measured by his own ends, has been almost completely short-circuited by man as applied to himself. But social, emotional, mental, and spiritual evolution are now carrying him on to ever greater complexity and awareness.

Men probably have not changed much in body shape and structure in the past twenty thousand years. Learning to chip flints, no job for an ape, probably took man most of the million years that he has been on earth, but he is moving faster now. The first creature to escape even partially from being a prisoner of the present, aware if at all only of the Everlasting Now, man is also the first to realize how far he has come along the path of coming alive, and to sense how much more alive he can become. Standing on the highest rung yet built on the ladder of life, faltering frequently, he is yet building still higher sections of the scaffold. This takes time.

No picture of creation is more inspiring than that of a beneficent Creator giving His creatures not a completed universe in which to dwell statically but a universe of ordered and progressive opportunity. Call the gropings of each living creature toward greater awareness blind or directed as you will, the result is the same—great new things under the sun.

Chapter Five

The Human Body

What is man? For the moment let us consider only his physical body, a delicate mechanism so complex yet so effective that the scientist, like the poet and the mystic, is awed when he contemplates it. Especially impressive is the human body as an integrated whole, which can do much more than is possible for the mere sum of its individual parts.

The body is a collection of thousands of servomechanisms working together in synchronized obedience to direction. It contains chemical factories that process molecules of countless varieties, breaking down those brought in from outside, taking energy from their parts, and resynthesizing them into new molecules with vastly superior abilities and functions. It is a little universe held at constant temperature, from which the forces of the outer world are kept for a time at bay, so that great new projects of living, never before attempted, can be carried out. It is the dwelling place, supporter, and protector of a brain that is the greatest tool yet developed by nature in her evolution. And it makes possible the emergence of the mind and the spirit of man.

When the body of a higher animal starts out as a fertilized egg, it immediately begins to divide, like an amoeba, but as its cells increase in numbers they cling together instead of drifting apart. Though at first these cells are all alike, because of the different chemical surroundings in which they find themselves those on the inside soon become different from those on the outside. Then, like boys influenced by their environments and their parents to become blacksmiths or politicians or policemen, the cells gradually begin to specialize. Each type of cell is soon making its own contribution to the body community, giving up a portion of its original freedom and flexibility for the sake of the benefits provided by an improved environment.

Like other cells, those of muscle consist of a cell wall filled with protoplasm that is always in a delicate equilibrium between remaining fluid and clotting. But as we have seen, fibrous strings of muscle cells have learned especially well to contract or relax. Anything that will release phosphate to the protoplasm from other molecules in the cell will cause its contents to congeal. The cell then contracts, and a muscle fiber made up of thousands of such cells will quickly shorten. A small electric shock, a chemical change, a temperature change, or even a mechanical pull, may be enough to trigger off this shrinkage. Thus is provided an admirable device for converting chemical energy into mechanical energy on receipt of a proper signal.

Once such specialized cells are available, organs can be built up from them to perform new functions.

Ages ago a remote ancestor of the earthworm developed a muscle-covered tube into the beginnings of a remarkable pump, which became the mammalian heart. In fact, this invention was probably made a dozen or so times quite independently, by creatures that stumbled onto its advantages in their mutational wanderings. Ultimately, in higher animals the heart developed into a very intricate and reliable mechanism. Though not the largest of mammalian hearts, that of a human being circulates 800 gallons of blood a day, and can be expected to operate for two billion pumping strokes or more without failure. This is more than ten times as many as we expect from any cylinder of an automobile engine.

A less appreciated though no less important organ than the heart is the kidney, a filter system and chemical control station invented when fishes were developed, and rightly credited by a famous biologist with making possible the later development of philosophers. These filters work continuously, sorting over our internal chemistry supplies some fifteen times a day. With many miles of tubes and strainers through which only certain needed types of molecules can pass, the kidney controls, among other things, the salt, amino-acid, and sugar levels in body fluids, the amount of water kept in the body, and the elimination of wastes.

Though it is not a mechanical pump, a kidney is a pump in the chemical sense, for it makes possible the keeping of the cells of the body bathed in fluids of a different level of salinity from the outside world. Thus can chemical insulation from the environment be provided for seventy years or so, in a sheltered haven where important new developments of nature can take place. Single-celled animals are at the mercy of any molecular debris that may be floating around in the water in which they find themselves. By perfecting the kidney, nature was able to build an organism inside out, putting its chemical environment within the creature, where it can be kept better under control, and surrounding it with a skin relatively impervious to undesirable molecules.

The main chemical distribution and communication system of the body, the blood stream, is a flowing assembly line that carries needed molecules to the various cells and organs and takes away waste. An average droplet of blood contains one hundred million or so red cells, about thirty thousand white cells, and a million or so flat platelets. Long ago nature learned the advantages of palletizing freight on barges, and the red blood cells carry oxygen as they float in the plasma

stream. Blood, sweat, and tears are all basically dependent
on this plasma, a kidney-perfected imitation of salt sea-water
as it was in the early days when the world's first cells were
floating in it.

The Mississippi at New Orleans would appear deserted
compared with the bustling arterial waterways of the body,
in which millions of tiny rafts bring molecular bales more
varied than the treasures of the Indies—oxygen, vitamins, hormones, glucose for energy, and raw materials with which to
build protein molecules. The rivers of the body are also filled
with old tires and orange peels—carbon dioxide journeying
to the lungs, and broken-down cells headed for the garbage
disposal organs. It carries too the white corpuscle guardian
cells and the antibody molecules to regions where foreign
cells or molecules may be invading the body. It even carries
a leak-proofing compound, fibrinogen, which heals any broken
pipes by forming a solid clot wherever a break occurs.

2

Viewing the body as a mechanism, an engineer is likely to
be most impressed with its intricate motor and control systems. Whenever man makes a new invention that he considers especially clever, he is likely to find that nature, millions of years previously, has anticipated him. This has been
true of his radar, his television camera, his electronic thermostat, his double-loop feedback mechanism, his high speed
digital computer. A tradition of accepting these as we find
them, as the marvelous handiwork of God, should not keep
us from appreciating their details, and interesting ourselves
in how they were developed. We must not discount Creation; it goes on about us constantly, and man has increasing
opportunity to take part in it.

The body is an exquisite motor, capable of moving itself and its parts about with great precision, and of remaining upright and balanced. It would be a rather clumsy machine if its parts were not so beautifully fitted and controlled, for the motions of walking are awkward as compared with the rolling of a wheel. Merely to stand erect involves the co-ordinated control of thousands of muscles, nerves, and bones.

Equally effective is the body as an energy converter. By burning extra food molecules in the tiny furnaces of his tissues, a man can do mechanical work for a short time at the rate of more than a horsepower, although his output falls off rapidly if the exertion must be kept up for long. Men have been measured producing one-half horsepower for twenty-two minutes while rowing a boat, one-fourth horse-power for several hours while climbing a mountain, and about one-sixth of a horsepower for a day at a time when walking.

Its neuro-muscular servomechanisms give the body amazing speed and dexterity. A piano virtuoso has been recorded as playing more than six thousand separate notes in slightly more than four minutes. This is more than twenty-four notes a second. Of course a number were played at the same time, but more than seventy new muscle combinations had to be put into action each second to do this.

To carry out so dexterous an operation requires that the performing mechanisms, the musician's hands, be governed by signals that travel very rapidly. A special chapter will be needed to discuss such communication and control mechanisms, of which the nervous systems of the human body represent the most effective type that exist. We shall look at the incredibly complex set of switchboards that forms the human brain and nervous system later, when we come to consider the mind of man.

The body, in addition to containing dozens of machines that are controlled by electro-mechanical servomechanisms that operate on the same principles as the often clumsier ones developed in recent years by scientists and engineers, also contains hundreds of control devices that operate chemically. These are the ductless glands, each of which produces one or more special kinds of molecules, the hormones, which when carried by the blood to other glands or organs greatly affect their behavior. One of the most remarkable developments of evolution is the subtle way in which an emotion, or even a thought, can increase or diminish the production of a particular kind of molecule, such as tears. Emotion and thought can also be greatly affected by the introduction of a new kind of molecule into the body.

In fact, emotion, or that which moves us, can be considered as a distilled essence arising from the interaction of molecules. However, this is not the simplest way to consider it, as we shall see later.

Fear or anger causes the adrenal glands, two quarter-ounce wrinkled peanuts of which one is perched atop each kidney, to send out extra adrenaline molecules, which put the whole body on the *qui vive* and release extra energy for emergency use. We would be in poor shape in a few days without some adrenaline, but in times of stress extra molecules of it float rapidly along the great communications channel of the blood stream until they reach tissues which need them. Each organ that needs adrenaline apparently pulls these molecules out with an automatic strainer or sorting mechanism, something like an IBM punched-card machine on the molecular scale. The newly arrived molecules change the activity of the liquid around and in the cells, and cleave some glycogen molecules into sugar so that their energy will be ready for immediate use. Besides adrenaline, the adrenal glands manufacture two dozen or more other kinds of special molecules.

The pituitary gland, no bigger than a mouse's ear, and tucked safely deep within the cranium, dumps hormones into the blood which act as chemical signals to inform a number of other glands how many of *their* hormone molecules to send out. Thus when the adrenal glands find in the blood an extra supply of the hormone called ACTH from the pituitary, they change the amount of cortisone they release to the blood, and as a result modify the actions of many organs. The pituitary gland seems to act as one of the general superintendents of the body's chemical factory, sending chemical orders to other glands which act as foremen, and thus indirectly bossing the rate of growth of many organs. When a tumor destroys a person's pituitary, his lips thicken and his features become coarser, his hair and teeth may begin to fall out, his muscles are weakened, sexual interest is diminished, blood pressure and body temperature are lowered, and many other undesirable results may ensue.

Among the best-known hormones, all of which are molecules of different shapes and sizes, are adrenaline, insulin, ACTH, cortisone, thyroxin, and the androgens and estrogens, male and female sex hormones. These molecules can all now be isolated and fed to individuals needing them. Until very recently, the pituitaries from five hundred thousand butchered hogs had to be used to collect a pound of ACTH, but fortunately this is enough to treat many patients. Now cortisone, adrenaline, and thyroxin can be completely synthesized from cheap and common atoms, and chemists hope soon to be able to build up all the hormone molecules from air, water, petroleum, amino-acids, and vitamins.

Despite the dependence of mind on matter thus revealed, the biologist who thought that mother love was merely manganese when he found that mother mice deprived of manganese in their diet no longer paid attention to their offspring, was not only jumping to a conclusion, but completely over it. Without manganese atoms the mouse's glands could not produce the proper hormone molecules to control those reactions of which mother love is one emotional expression. Though removing an atom may remove an emotion, this does not make them identical. It would be equally senseless to say that pity is phosphorus, or justice oxygen. Yet without oxygen, phosphorus, and some dozens of other atoms, there can be neither justice nor mercy.

3

We think of our bodies as permanent over a lifetime, but they are as the shifting sands of the desert, with atoms and molecules continually being removed and replaced with new ones. Studies with tracer elements show that fewer than 2 percent of the atoms that a body contains were present during the previous year. Throughout life, we have the bodies we started with only in the sense that the New Englander had his genuine pre-Revolutionary ax, which had had seven new handles and three new heads. Often atoms wander into our bodies that we have used before, for a human body takes in many more atoms in a year than there are spoonsful of water in the entire world. Time is a great mixer, and in this century one can be fairly sure that his body contains some of the atoms, and perhaps even some of the actual molecules, that made up the body of Caesar, or Washington, or Omar Khayyám.

To keep this humming factory in operation, the body must be fed raw materials. Most urgently needed is oxygen, to combine with food molecules and release energy from them. Few parts of the body can be safely starved of oxygen for more than a few minutes. A whale, as a result of special lung development, can store enough oxygen for a half-hour dive. A lungfish, by remaining in a coma and turning himself into an almost motionless lump that takes but a few shallow breaths a day, can stay imprisoned in mud for five years, but if the measure of living is awareness he can only be said to be carrying out a holding operation.

Almost three-quarters of the human body is water, and nearly half of these water molecules are changed each week. At least three pints of water must go through the body every day to keep its atom-sorting and assembly lines running. To provide this we each drink about 200 gallons of water a year, whether as water, coffee, milk, or wine. Since the body holds several gallons of water there is less immediate urgency in obtaining a new supply than in the case of oxygen, and people seldom die of thirst in less than a week. Stored water need not be in liquid form; its atomic parts can be held locked in fat molecules, as in the camel's hump, or even in hair, which will slake the woolly thirst of an infant moth.

Next in urgency to water the body needs energy to keep it warm, to provide for the mechanical activities of the muscles, and to operate its chemical and mechanical machines, the organs. This energy is brought in stored in molecules of the carbohydrates, fats, and proteins. Fat molecules are fairly simple, and are made by joining three fatty-acid molecules to one of glycerol. Starch and glycogen are made by fastening together sugar molecules in long chains with side branches. The proteins we have met as extremely complex co-operative colonies of thousands of atoms. All these molecules make fine slow-burning fuels when combined with oxygen.

The body of a person of average size, if he is willing to stay in bed all the time, will be moderately well nourished if he digests every day food carrying 1700 calories of energy. An active person is likely to need 2800 calories, however, and a man doing hard physical work as many as 4500. Though the body needs little energy when resting, the process of tearing down and building up its cells goes on continously.

If it lacks starch and sugar it starts to break down the fat molecules that are stored in it as reservoirs of energy. When these get scarce it digests some of its own protein molecules, so that it begins to resemble a house kept warm by burning its own paneling. A man consuming his own cells internally can keep alive for from thirty to sixty days without eating.

If calories were all we needed, we could each live on 1.5 pounds of sugar a day, or 7.5 pounds of potatoes, or 1 pound of butter or lard. Any of these would take care of the fuel requirements of our personal factory, but we need also bricks and mortar to keep it in repair. To build up new cells we need certain amino-acids that our bodies cannot synthesize. The body produces these by tearing down to their amino-acid sub-parts protein molecules taken from the bodies of animals or plants. To keep our daily food intake in proper balance we need a little more than a pound of basic carbohydrates for energy, about three ounces of fat for the same purpose, and slightly more than three ounces of protein for construction of molecules and cells. This pound and a half of dry material we bulk out with more than three pounds of water to give the five pounds or so of food we each consume in a day.

One human body may contain a hundred thousand different kinds of protein molecules—many trillions of each variety. Typical proteins are collagen, which provides framework material; hemoglobin, which carries oxygen in the blood cells; keratin, contained in the protective cells of hair, skin, and fingernails; myosin, which converts energy from chemical to mechanical form in muscle cells; and the specialized enzymes and hormones so important in regulating body activity.

The protein molecules taken in with food to furnish these body proteins are not, when being digested, torn down completely to their constituent atoms, but are separated by enzymes merely into their sub-molecules, the amino-acids.

At least eight kinds of these acids are called essential because our bodies cannot make them, but if we can get these our enzymes can, by rearranging their parts, make the needed additional dozen or so.

Because large protein molecules are delicate, it is not easy to break one into its amino-acid parts without an enzyme. Boiling for a full day in strong acid is one way to do this, but the acid is likely to dissolve too many bonds, including some of the wrong ones. Enzyme molecules attack the proper bonds individually, as though taking the molecule apart with a screw driver instead of a sledge hammer.

To produce these enzymes the body uses vitamins. Most important among these are Vitamin A, which keeps the eyes functioning correctly; Vitamin C, which prevents scurvy; Vitamin D, which prevents rickets; and a whole group of more than a dozen B vitamins, which were discovered only after the letter B had been assigned to what turned out to be a wide variety of molecules, including niacin, thiamin, and riboflavin.

In addition to molecules made from simple atoms found everywhere in air and water, our bodies need small quantities of certain heavier and scarcer atoms with which to build highly specialized molecules. About a pound of calcium a year is needed for bones and teeth, to stiffen cell walls, and to help milk to curdle and blood to clot. Roughly a pound of iron is needed in a lifetime, to build hemoglobin molecules that carry oxygen in the red blood cells. Still heavier "trace elements," like zinc and molybdenum and cobalt, are needed in minute quantities to build specific enzyme and hormone molecules. Most of these we get automatically if we eat a balanced and varied diet, but sometimes an accidental scarcity of one produces illness.

4

The number of human beings that can live on earth at one time is limited, not by space in which to dwell, but by the amount of food the earth can be made to yield. Never in history has everyone had enough to eat. To fill completely all the needs of its present two and a half billion inhabitants, the good earth would somehow have to yield a quarter again as much as it now supplies for nourishment.

Since our fathers were born the number of living persons has been increasing three times as fast as the amount of food produced. Every day at dinnertime one hundred thousand new mouths, born since yesterday, arrive to be fed. One of the most poorly nourished populations is that of India, yet every year five million tiny Indians come into a world unable to keep their bodies from emaciation. Within a generation the food supply of the world will have to be doubled if all humans are to be fed properly.

All nourishment that keeps the animal world alive must first be stored by plants, for plants alone have learned to capture energy from the sun. Each year the living plants of earth form some 360 billion tons of sugars and starches, and set free more than 400 billion tons of oxygen needed for breathing by animals.

The world's heaviest food crop is potatoes, but four-fifths of a potato is water and ash. Sugar cane, whose grassy cells have been trained to specialize in storing sweets, has reached the world's record as the most effective producer of calories, at 40 tons of food and fuel per acre per year, but it can be grown only in a warm and humid climate, and this record is set in Hawaii where cane can grow the year around. On the American mainland the most important food plant is corn, a once ineffective grass that was nearly extinct when men came along and, by selecting seeds and mixing genetic strains, made it superior to even such valuable molecule-builders as wheat and oats.

Raising animals for food is less efficient than raising plants, for some sort of plant must be raised first anyway, and animals hold in their flesh only small fractions of the calories they consume in fodder and grain. Most efficient of all converters of plant into animal proteins is the milk cow; some well-bred cows give back in dairy products almost a quarter of all the calories they eat, storing proteins for their offspring more than twice as efficiently as for themselves. More effective as a meat producer is the hog, in whose ham, bacon, and other parts one is likely to find nearly a fifth of the calories it fed upon. Steers and sheep give back as useful meat less than one-tenth of what they eat, which makes meat-raising seem hardly worthwhile, but such animals can be pastured on land too poor to grow food for human consumption, and their fats, hides, and wool help to balance the books. The basic reason that raising animals for meat pays is that bacteria in their digestive tracts enable them to convert into nourishing food grass and roughage unsuited to human use. The rumen of a steer contains many gallons of warm water in which nourishing chemicals encourage bacteria to swarm by the billions. These organisms secrete enzymes that attack the cellulose and other molecules in hay and grass and rearrange some of them into molecules the animal, and later man, can use.

Of the present nourishment needs of man, the greatest is for more foods containing protein molecules of kinds whose atomic bonds can easily be dissolved by the enzymes in the human digestive system, so that their parts can be rearranged to build the cells and tissues of human bodies. Plants build up many such proteins especially for storage in their seeds, and humans who are strict vegetarians can be nourished well enough. It is good, however, for the human stomach to receive some meat, for animal proteins are rich in certain aminoacids that are necessary for life, which proteins of vegetable origin may lack. It is useful to let animals preconcentrate a portion of the bulk of vegetation. To get from peas or beans molecules equivalent to those that are obtained from the 140 pounds of meat most Americans swallow in a year would require that each consume about 400 pounds of legumes. Eight ounces of dry skim milk yields as much protein as 24 ounces of soy bean meal.

The desire of vegetarians not to utilize the bodies of animals for food is overly sentimental and rather illogical, for the living world exists only by passing molecules from the body of one dead creature to another that is alive, for rearrangement and temporary utilization of their constituents. The parts of any given protein molecule may well be used by dozens of creatures before separating finally into the atoms of which it is composed.

Infant creatures of any species grow much faster than adults, and need molecules that carry energy and basic building materials in quickly available form. Nature has done wonders in learning to concentrate nourishment for their use. The yolks of a nestful of robin eggs contain such a fine array and balance of foodstuffs that when the eggs hatch into a wriggling mass of open mouths, cell multiplication can proceed with incredible speed. Young birds that have used up their internal store of food have been observed being fed by their parents as many as a thousand times a day, and a biologist found that a robin just out of the nest ate fourteen feet of earthworms between dawn and evening's end.

Many of our most important food products, such as seeds, fruits, and especially milk and eggs, represent concentrated stores laid by especially for infant nourishment. Milk is to man an even more important natural food than eggs. A pint of milk yields ten times as much calcium as a pound of eggs (unless one eats the shells) and contains additional vitamins. Though a liquid, as developed to suit toothless infants (or are infants toothless because milk is a liquid?) milk curdles into a solid as soon as it reaches the stomach. In fact, it contains more solids per quart than equal weights of such rigid objects as tomatoes, lettuce, and watermelons.

Though few plants are now harvested from the sea, vegetation growing in the sunny upper layers of earth's oceans stores nine times the nourishment captured by all the plants on land together. An acre of water is likely to grow three times as many tons of plant cells as any acre ashore, and the earth has three times as much sea as land. In fact, two hundred times the nourishment our hungry world now needs decays, unharvested, in the greenhouses of the sea. Scientists are working on the problem of making it available to man.

It is possible that the efficiency of farming might be raised by substituting for land plants, with their complex root, leaf and branch systems that store more fuel than food, simple algae having single cells, of which eighteen thousand species are known. Of these many types are digestible, brimming with nourishment, and packed with vitamins. Through rapid selective breeding, strains of algae have been developed which contain as much as 55 percent protein, and others up to 85 percent of fat. Such a crop can be made to double its weight in ten hours.

Unfortunately, though more nutritious than tomatoes or strawberries, algae do not taste so good, and food products made from them are usually described as "acceptable." Even so, algae flour is now sold regularly in several foreign cities, usually mixed with ordinary flour, to which it gives a somewhat bilious tinge. But the world is not yet sufficiently hungry to consider really tasty the "delicate grassy flavor" of algae, and much scientific work remains to be done before its products can be converted on an economic basis into either real or synthetic steaks.

Many land plants on which equal amounts of loving care and expensive equipment were lavished would probably store energy as fast and as efficiently as algae. Though not so much is heard about hydroponics today as fifteen years ago, this system of growing vegetables in nutrient solutions instead of soil still offers useful possibilities. By merely improving ordinary farming we have already increased our crop outputs from a given acreage of land in the United States by one-third since 1920, and less than half as much labor is now required to produce a ton of food as was needed then.

Catching more of the bountiful supply of energy that reaches our earth, and storing it effectively in complex molecules for food, is a problem that can be solved. But science, as a great humanistic endeavor, must be applied to full capacity if mankind is thus to be enabled to move in the direction of a fuller life.

5

When King Charles II of England died less than three hundred years ago, the royal physicians could truthfully announce that they had done everything "possible" to save his life. But of the forty-three different things they tried, from raising blisters on the King's head to applying a plaster of pitch and pigeon dung to his feet, the only effective one was to make his majesty feel that they were trying to cure him. These doctors just didn't know how the King's body was constructed, or what added molecules would help to eliminate his disease. Today physicians are learning to attack illness at the level on which it originates, and a surgeon operates to cure a headache only when the ache is caused by a mechanical difficulty. The saving of millions of lives by new kinds of molecules is a part of the improved control of our environment that science brings.

Upsets of balance within the body can be mechanical, chemical, or organic. Diseases can arise from lacks of specific atoms or molecules, or from invasion by foreign bodies such as viruses, or microorganisms which may in turn be plants or animals. Then there may be uncontrolled growth of the body's own cells in abnormal forms, a subject only beginning to be understood. Finally there is the slow degeneration that takes place in various organs, which gradually diminishes their responsiveness to signals and their ability to perform their normal functions.

Diseases that result from a lack of specific atoms or molecules are now under good control. Before the importance of drinking lime juice or eating a fresh fruit or vegetable every day was recognized in the eighteenth century, scurvy was one of the most common diseases in Europe. Now twenty-two cents' worth of Vitamin C a year, if necessary synthesized directly from cheap atoms, will keep anyone scurvyless. Again, rickets can be prevented completely by a few cents' worth of Vitamin D.

Deficiency diseases of another class result when some gland of the body no longer manufactures the correct amounts of the kinds of molecules it provides for body operation. Insulin, made by the pancreas, controls the level of body sugar, and if too few insulin molecules are produced diabetes results. It was a great day for patients with advanced diabetes when it was found that they need not die if given a daily supply of insulin molecules. Though control of this disease is not yet perfect, its contribution to the death rate has been cut in half.

Diseases of another great class result from invasion of the

body by microscopic enemies of three kinds: large protein molecules or groups of molecules, the viruses; single-celled plants, the bacteria and molds; and single-celled animals, the protozoa. Hostile organisms of all three types are always present in the body and its surroundings, but are kept from multiplying profusely by the defenses of the body—especially by the microbe-fighting white blood cells and antibodies. Let some part of the body chemistry go out of balance or some special function deteriorate, and the microorganisms are likely to multiply at a terrific rate. They then upset the body chemistry further, and we are sick.

Early in this century it was not uncommon for diphtheria to kill several children in a family within a single week. At the temperature of the human body diphtheria plants can produce five billion new cells in a day, and these give off molecules that are very poisonous to the body. In fact, the toxins produced in infectious diseases are often enzymes quite similar to the poisons secreted by many snakes and insects. Now diphtheria, being understood, can be brought under complete control.

New molecules that the body cells can tolerate in quantities that the bacteria cells themselves find poisonous are working wonders in controlling infectious diseases. Of the drugs used today, fewer than a third existed in 1940. More than five hundred new drugs, each a valuable new molecule, are launched for use each year. A great step forward was the discovery of the sulfa drugs, molecules of many types ranging from sulfanilamide to sulfadiazine, which the more dangerous kinds of bacteria were found to dislike heartily. Within a very few years these drugs were overshadowed by the still more powerful antibiotics, such as penicillin and aureomycin, special molecules synthesized by certain microorganisms to kill other microorganisms that trespass on their home territory. Many molds and other types of cell life that live in soils and other lowly environments have learned to synthesize such molecules to keep other types of cells away. Some such antibiotics are specific against only one or two kinds of undesirable microorganisms, while others are more mildly repellent to a great variety of trespassers.

One of the midnight terrors of parents only a few years ago was the earache of a feverish child, and worry over a dangerous mastoid operation that might be needed. Now, as a result of the new molecules, many young surgeons have never seen a mastoid operation. Again, yaws is a terrible tropical disease that formerly affected half the population in parts of the West Indies, yet the use of thirty cents' worth of penicillin per person reduced its prevalence in three years to about 1 percent. Shortly after penicillin was discovered one hundred thousand units of it cost twenty dollars to make; within a few years its price had fallen to six cents, and the death rate from pneumonia in the United States had been cut in half.

Though many bacteria are killed by sulfa drug or antibiotic molecules, the descendants of those bacteria that are somewhat immune can gradually learn not to mind the poison at all, and even to like it. It is now found best to keep such drugs away from bacteria unless they are sure to be killed by them, for any bacteria that survive are likely to found a race of increasingly resistant successors, just as some insects are learning to tolerate DDT. Strains of staphylococcus bacteria in certain hospitals where much penicillin is used are said to be ten times as resistant to it now as their country cousins. Thousands of generations, which occupy only a few years in the bacterial world, enable them to learn to synthesize enzymes that counteract the effects of the antibiotics.

Malaria, which results from invasion of the blood stream by single-celled animals, is a good example of how a disease can be attacked by molecules on various levels. A hundred million people still suffer from malaria in India alone, and a million a year die from it there. Yet it could be completely eradicated by the use of several kinds of molecules not yet common in India. First DDT, with another molecule to use on insects that are not harmed by it, could be used to kill off the special mosquitoes that transmit malaria. Then the malaria germs that had entered human blood streams could be killed off with quinine or one of its more effective successors, atabrine or primaquine.

Viruses in general are not affected by antibiotics. Neither penicillin nor streptomycin bothers the viruses that cause the common cold, but they can hold down the numbers of the bacteria that tend to grow in a body weakened by viruses. The healthy body has a very effective system for producing antibodies, molecules in the blood which can combine chemically with viruses and neutralize them. The large protein molecules called gamma globulin appear able to change their atomic patterns to neutralize almost any type of invading molecule, and will multiply rapidly in the form needed to repel a particular invasion. In the present great fight against polio, medical men are seeking further ways of helping the human system develop these antibodies.

Nervous and mental diseases are our greatest cause of disability today, and in the United States cost more than ten billion dollars a year in loss of social wealth. There are now some six hundred fifty thousand mental patients in public hospitals, and more beds are needed for them than for all those who have other diseases together. That a great increase in nervous and mental breakdowns has resulted from the complexities of modern living is denied by many outstanding psychiatrists, however. They say that every family, no matter how distinguished, can be found to have many mental and nervous invalids among its progenitors, and that this has always been

the case. Some mental diseases originate from actual structural changes in the brain, others are doubtless caused by
chemical changes, and still others by emotional and mental
upheavals, but these are all interrelated. Several new drugs,
among them chlorpromazine and reserpine, show much prom-
ise of aiding the mentally ill.

All humans show in some degree the symptoms of emotional and mental illness. We all daydream like the schizophrenic or are abnormally self-conscious like the paranoid,
but usually these tendencies are held under control. Many
of our minor ills are undoubtedly caused by emotional difficulties. One person will eat more when disturbed, another
less. Thus, a father whose daughter was causing worry lost
thirteen pounds in three weeks, while his wife, similarly upset, gained twenty-six pounds.

6

If the body were built like the "wonderful one-hoss shay"
we might all expect, within a few years, to live well into
the nineties. But our physical system does not age uniformly
in all its parts. One physician stated that at twenty-five he
had old hair, while at sixty-six he still had young teeth.
Death comes when any vital member of the organic partner-
ship can no longer carry out its proper function. Which
particular colony of cells will fail first depends on how good
a job of directing the organization of matter one's personal
genes can do, and on the circumstances of one's life. We are
getting better control over these circumstances. But even
if accidents and diseases were eliminated, some organ could
be expected to begin to fail in every individual before many
years more than one hundred had passed after his birth.

The longest human life span ordinarily quoted as verifiable is that of Thomas Parr, an Englishman of the seventeenth century, who is supposed to have lived to be one hundred fifty-two. This turns out to be another of those interesting items that is quoted from author to author without verification, and now appears to have been disproved. About one hundred fifteen years is probably the longest certified human span, and this maximum appears not to have changed much over recent centuries.

The average life span on earth of an individual has been greatly lengthened, however, and for a number of decades now life expectancy has been increasing in the United States by the amazing figure of five extra years in every ten. Every newborn baby today can be expected to have at least twice as many days of life as it would have had if born at the end of the American Revolution.

In the earliest days of history most human bodies lasted only about eighteen years. By the time Rome was a city this figure had risen to twenty-two years for its inhabitants. The general increase during recorded history of the average length of life in the countries where science is most advanced has been almost fourfold. Civilization has existed on earth for only about three hundred generations, but man has existed as man for more than thirty thousand generations. Even so, it has been calculated that one out of every twenty men who have ever lived is alive today. The time may well arrive when a tenth of all the souls of men, in the strictly Biblical sense, will be inhabiting mortal bodies at one time.

In such ancient and unmodern cultures as those of Egypt and India the life expectancy at birth is still only thirty years. Almost three times as many children are born to a given number of parents in India each year as in the United States, and about three times as many die. Thus approximately three times as much effort goes into the production of a given number of man-years of human life in a nonscientific en-

vironment. In countries whose inhabitants subsist on agri-
culture about fifteen out of every one hundred persons born
last to the age of sixty, but as a result of scientific advances,
in those having industrial economies this figure has risen to
seventy out of one hundred, or almost five times as many.

Although much of our increased longevity arises from a
reduction in infant mortality to one-fourth of what it was
previously, diseases of youth and middle-age are also now
under much better control. With current gains in the wars
on microbes, the most serious causes of death that remain are
those arising from accidental injuries, those that represent uncontrolled growth of cells, and those that arise from the loss
of function of body parts, the degenerative diseases such as
hardening of the arteries.

The replacement of organs in the body with new tissue
from other bodies that no longer need them has in the past
been limited by subtle factors that seemed impossible to control. An example of how several separate strides forward in
medical science can result in great progress is given by the
recent new operations in which large blood vessels have been
replaced. The aorta, big as a garden hose where it connects
to the heart, tends with the arteries in some persons to become
thick-walled, stiff, and clogged, which throws a greatly increased load on the pumping muscles, and dangerous pressures on tubes and valves connected to it. Damaged parts
of this living tube can sometimes be replaced today with
fresh pieces, and dozens of persons are now walking around
with new sections of aortas in their bodies. This has become
possible only as a result of five new simultaneous developments.

Such a serious operation as replacing a section of aorta
usually requires several hours under complete anesthesia,
and few patients could be expected to withstand the effects
of the several pounds of ether previously needed. Now
nearly a hundred anesthetics are available, many of them spe-

cialist molecules that block off consciousness, kill pain, or restrain body movements. With these a ten-hour operation can be carried out with comparative safety while the patient's feelings and responses are controlled by a skilled anesthesiologist, turning valves like an organist playing on a complex console.

Equally important is the improved control the surgeon has of the contents of the patient's blood stream during the operation and after. Glucose and salt solutions, blood plasma, and various other materials are dripped into his system to maintain proper chemical balance, and prevent him from going into shock as a result of the sudden chemical changes that occurred previously when much blood was lost.

Necessary also is the new possibility brought about by physicists with their atom-smashing particle accelerators, of dropping electrons over a several-million volt precipice and then hurling them against matter. Tissues to be grafted into the body can be sterilized by such electrons without damage. After bombardment with high-speed electrons a collection of aortas can be frozen and kept sterile for use at a later time. When the tubular graft has been sewed in place, antibiotics and sulfa drugs spread on the wounds help keep infection down until the body's own cells can control this.

All of these improved procedures would still have been of no avail, however, if it were not for another advance. The protein molecules of the grafted aorta, having come from the body of another person, are treated as foreign objects by the cells of the patient's blood, and are disposed of as so much garbage as rapidly as possible. To hasten the formation of new cells about the borrowed aorta before the body can dissolve all of its foreign tissue, the surgeon brushes on the wounds material made from fibrinogen, a clotting agent of the blood. This speeds the formation of new cells, and by the time the borrowed aorta has disappeared, a new one has been formed from the body's own cells to replace it. The patient by this time is walking around in much better health.

Why should bodies ever die? If they are made of atoms that last for billions of years, which are in any case replaced every few months, why can they not last a million years or more? Personal immortality, even in a physical sense, has long seemed of utmost importance to mortal man. The reasons men's bodies are not immortal are to be sought in the levels of organization of the cell.

Cells themselves are thought by many biologists to be capable of a fair degree of immortality, although this cannot be considered as proved. Living tissues, such as heart tissue from a chick embryo, have been kept growing for many years in solutions in glass bottles. The cells are found to multiply indefinitely so long as they are kept at the proper temperature, waste products are removed, and new nourishing molecules are supplied as needed. Similarly, single-celled organisms, like the amoeba or paramecium, are sometimes said to be immortal, for barring accidents each individual ends by splitting up into two new ones without otherwise disappearing. A single strain of paramecia has been watched for nine thousand generations, and the last ones seemed as fresh, young, and vigorous as the Adam of their race. But it may be questioned whether cells of this sort really are immortal, even in a restricted sense. In the case cited the grandfather nine thousand times removed had lived only fourteen years before, and no cell colonies have been kept growing in glass bottles for more than a few dozen years. The cells in our own bodies show signs of deterioration long before we are through with them at the allotted threescore years and ten.

The rate of multiplication of cells in a body slows down greatly after the first few generations; otherwise most colonies of cells, if nourished as individuals apart and allowed to proliferate, would grow to man size in a few days after the first cell division. It may well be that a gradual deterioration of cell structure sets in over the span of a human lifetime.

Perhaps the cells slowly lose the ability to change from mobile to fixed, and take on a set, so that there is a decrease in response to external stimuli, and a diminishing tendency to divide into new cells. As the cells of our bodies are continually being replaced, it would appear that the basic causes of human mortality lie in deterioration of an integrating and functioning ability that controls the production of new cells and their interrelationships, perhaps combined with changes in the cells themselves.

Even if surgeons could learn to patch up our bodies indefinitely by transplanting new organs from a central stock as rapidly as the originals wore out, which is very unlikely, and kept these functioning as a unit so that a given brain could be kept operating for, say, two hundred years instead of an average of sixty-eight, the gift of the extra years of life would be less valuable than we are inclined to think. Wisdom and experience accumulate in an individual, to be sure, but there is also an accretion of prejudices and traditional behavior that resists the change that nature finds so valuable. The actions of a brain take on a set analogous to the accumulation of insoluble materials in a cell. The beneficent fluxes of nature dissolve such deposits in their own way, returning their substance to the basic store, and perpetuating their accomplishments in the development of the human spirit and the consciousness of the race.

We should not trouble our minds unduly about fundamental limitations on the human span to ninety or a hundred. The great purpose of scientific knowledge, as of knowledge from all sources, should be to make the years of our lives of the greatest beauty and value to the individual and to the race. Science can also continue to increase the number of human lives that can be brought to experience in this great and interesting world. In this sense, as in many others, it has already become one of man's greatest humanistic achievements.

Chapter Six

The Nesting Place for Life

To form the living bodies of new kinds of plants and animals by the processes of evolution, vast stretches of time are needed. To reach any sort of complexity at all requires, in a turbulent universe like ours, a peaceful haven that will remain calm, in an atomic sense, over billions of years. If the surroundings in which molecules are to gather into living forms are too hot, they will soon be shaken apart. If the surroundings are too cold, the chemical reactions that govern the shifting of atoms from molecule to molecule will take place so slowly that little evolution can occur in a cosmic cycle of any reasonable length. Setting things up to provide a physical world in which life can appear requires a nice adjustment of temperature, even before the dozens of other necessary factors are considered.

Our planet Earth has proved an ideal nest for life, warm enough to permit human bodies and brains to be developed from primordial matter in two or three billion years, yet not so hot that molecules which gathered to form the cells of a jellyfish or oyster were parboiled and dispersed. Though we no longer believe that the earth is necessarily the only spot in the universe that has been honored as a host to living forms, with our limited means of exploration we know of no other location having conditions so favorable for the orderly and systematic arrangement of atoms into living bodies.

Some philosophers say that the earth appears to us to be an almost ideal spot for the development of living creatures merely because we define life in terms of what we find on earth. There may, indeed, be other kinds of life which we have not yet recognized, but the body of every living creature of which man knows was formed from atoms of only a few varieties, and depends for its existence on the properties of those atoms.

When light from the stars is dissected by the spectroscope it reveals that no body visible in the heavens is made of other atoms than those we know on earth. Our entire universe appears to be built of them. Within limits, they can be expected under similar conditions to obey the laws of physics and chemistry that atoms obey on earth. The varieties of molecules that can be built with such atoms are limited in number, and their properties that make possible the building of living forms are still more seriously limited. The complexities and stability needed for even the simplest life demand properties possessed by only a few atoms, and our knowledge of atomic structure shows that additional varieties of atoms, able to enter into different but equally complex patterns, are not likely to exist.

We can imagine that fiery creatures may inhabit the hot reaches of the sun, or even its hotter interior, but they could not be of forms even remotely related to any life we know, and their bodies could not be made of molecules. Few molecules can remain intact in such heat, and those that can are so small and so strongly self-contained as to offer little possibility of the delicate energy exchanges that support life in earth's plants and animals.

Water molecules serve every living creature as a solvent sea to carry building blocks about within its body. Obviously neither plants nor animals could grow in surroundings where all the water needed for their sap or blood would congeal into ice crystals or vaporize as steam. This requirement limits a nest for life to a maximum temperature of 212°F, and a minimum of 32°F. A few kinds of bacteria are found able to stay alive if kept at 300°F below zero for a time, and when warmed again will grow and multiply, but their animation is suspended while frozen. At the other extreme, algae of a few special types are found to prosper in hot springs, but only at temperatures up to 185°F.

The higher animals can flourish only in a range of temperatures much narrower than that in which water is liquid, and nature keeps their complex protein molecules from being shaken apart or congealed with a remarkable series of thermostats that hold such creatures' inner baths of blood to a steady healthy temperature. Birds, all rapid livers since they took on the exhausting but rewarding job of flying, need rapid chemical activity, and their blood streams are maintained at temperatures between 110° and 113°F. The thermostats of most of the other warm-blooded animals are set slightly lower, usually near the 98° to 99°F at which the organs in a human body are held.

Before nature reached the high stage at which she was able to develop the mechanisms needed to maintain constant internal body temperatures in an animal, outside temperature conditions had to be held fairly constant over billions of years. A resting place in space had to be provided on which molecules could remain relatively undisturbed, while carefully metered energy from the sun sent them through the seemingly endless convolutions that eventually patterned them into genes, amoebas, carrots, ants, and men.

All the other planets of our solar system, perhaps excepting Mars, have one or more characteristics obviously sufficient to prevent the development of life in any way like ours. As man sits up and rubs his scientific eyes he cannot fail to be impressed by the number of circumstances that appear to have conspired to make his existence possible.

The fact that dozens of conditions must together be fulfilled if life is to develop, and that all of these are found fulfilled on earth, indicates to many persons the direct beneficent hand of a Creator. Others believe instead that the needed combination of circumstances happens to be available on earth by pure chance, and that whatever could grow here has grown. Many take an intermediate position, feeling that the innate desire of most humans to visualize a beneficent power can still be fulfilled without contradicting what science shows, if God is not visualized too closely in the image of man.

Of one thing we can be sure: a perfect world was not created out of hand. Rather in this our universe an opportunity was provided, at least on planet Earth (and we like to think elsewhere as well), to work toward the perfection of ever more complex creatures, creatures of increasing potentiality of action and accomplishment, within the time a solar system can be kept in action. Science shows that we were born into a world governed by discoverable laws, and that by working within these laws any creature has almost unbounded opportunity for new attainment.

2

Anthropologists believe that creatures recognizable as men have roamed the earth for more than a million years. Since this is more than a hundred times as long as human history reaches back, it is fair to ask how scientists can be so sure as they seem to be of the age of a skull or a bone implement, to say nothing of a continent, or the earth or solar system. Geologists have in the past been forced frequently to revise their estimates of the age of a fossil trilobite or a glacial deposit, and usually found them older than they had thought.

Recently very reliable dating methods have become available. These involve clocks that keep time in terms of the atoms themselves. Of the one thousand or so isotope varieties of the one hundred one kinds of atoms thus far discovered, some, as we have seen, are so stable that they can be expected to last for the duration of the universe, while others are shorter-lived. Many chemical elements have isotopes covering a wide range of stabilities, from those whose newly formed atoms will almost all have exploded within a few thousandths of a second, to those whose atoms do not explode at all.

The exact time at which an atom will explode can never be predicted in advance, but the average lifetime of a large group of similar atoms can be predicted more accurately than that of a large group of men. The fraction of any large number that will have exploded within a given span of seconds, months, or centuries, is definite for an isotopic species. The half-life of an isotope, as we have seen, is that period of time during which a pound of it will have been reduced to half a pound, a half-pound to a quarter, or any number of atoms to half that number.

By determining the relative amounts of two or more isotopes of an atom in a sample of material, one can date the time of its formation or mixing. Often several different isotope-ratios can be used to time the same occurrence, and when all indicate approximately the same date, confidence in the correctness of the estimate goes up immensely.

Wherever uranium ore is dug on earth, or taken from meteorites, 138 times as many atoms of the U 238 isotope are found as of U 235. The atoms of U 238 in any sample are found to explode at a rate which would destroy half of

them in four and a half billion years, while half of those of
U 235 would explode in seven hundred million years. Thus as
time progresses more of the U 235 atoms blow up than of the
others, and the U 238 atoms come increasingly to predomi-
nate. The ratio 138 to 1 for Uranium 238/235 gives a time
of about six billion years that has elapsed since they were
nearly equal.

The ratios of other long-lived atomic isotopes give approximately the same date of creation of their atoms. U 235
atoms, with their half-life of seven hundred million years, explode to form lead atoms which remain stable, and the
amounts of each found in undisturbed ores give a date of
about five billion years. Similar ages are obtained when
the relative abundances of many other kinds of exploding
atoms are measured.

As these new dating methods have become available to
supplement older ones, such as determination of the amount
of salt in the sea and the rate of erosion of land, our earth
has been found to be more than twice as old as the two billion years given it as recently as thirty years ago by most
geologists.

Lesser events than the Creation can also be effectively
dated by choosing isotopes with half-lives in the proper range,
from a few hundred to a few billion years. The relative
abundances of rubidium and strontium isotopes indicate that
certain ore bodies in different parts of the earth's surface were
laid down at periods ranging from three billion to ten million
years ago. Helium atoms are formed in rocks containing
radioactive atoms, and sampling the amount of helium in a
hard rock gives a good measure of its age if it is younger than
ten million and older than thirty thousand years.

Most striking is a method recently devised with which
the date at which an object living long centuries ago ceased
to breathe can be determined. This involves measurement of

the amount of the Carbon 14 isotope contained in the remnants of plants and animals. C 14 is a rare and temporary variety of carbon atom which enters indistinguishably with ordinary permanent carbon, C 12, into the structure of living matter, but is unstable, with a half-life of only 5568 years. At the top of the atmosphere C 14 atoms are constantly being produced when the nuclei of nitrogen atoms are struck by neutrons produced by energetic cosmic rays. These new atoms spread uniformly through the atmosphere, and like ordinary carbon, join oxygen atoms to form CO_2. Every plant in its transpiration takes in some of these explosive atoms, not enough to do it harm, but enough so that they can be measured. They enter into all the living cells, including those of animals which consume the plants. While a plant or animal is alive, the fraction of C 14 atoms among a given number of carbon atoms remains the same through constant exchange, but when the creature dies and its remnants are isolated from the air by mud, etc., the number of C 14 atoms remaining in it continually diminishes as more and more explode, and the C 14/C 12 ratio gets smaller as the sample gets older.

The fraction of carbon atoms which are C 14 remaining in a chunk of wood or bone can be determined by measuring with a Geiger counter the number exploding per second for each ounce of carbon in the specimen. Unfortunately this is not so simple a determination as one would wish, for cosmic rays that strike the measuring counter give almost as much response as the few atoms that explode in a short time in a very old specimen of organic material. However, by putting a heavy iron shield around the measuring apparatus, it is possible to reduce the interfering clicks enough to measure to within a few hundred years the ages of samples up to thirty thousand years old. This dating system can be tied in with the older method of dating logs by measuring the thicknesses of successive tree rings. Together they can be used to tie man's written history to that revealed by the rocks and stars.

3

Returning now to our waiting planet, we have assumed it ready to serve as a nesting place on which life can in time develop. To urge some of its lifeless atoms and molecules toward collecting into higher forms, energy must be provided, and this can best be obtained as radiant photons from a hot star that lies near enough to act as a warming sun. To be suitable for sunhood a star must be at such a temperature that it will emit radiant energy containing many photons of sizes in the range that can be safely absorbed by the more complex stable molecules of living matter. These photons are carried by light waves lying in that part of the spectrum which our eyes can see. Many stars are so hot that they emit enough large photons of ultraviolet light and X-rays to tear apart living molecules absorbing them, unless by some means these dangerous photons are removed. Cool stars, on the other hand, radiate mostly infrared and microwave rays, whose photons are too small to enable atoms to rearrange themselves into molecules complex enough to form living creatures. The surface temperature of our own sun is ideal, for it emits radiation having photons of just the right sizes to stimulate the outer electrons of the atoms and molecules of our universe, and enable them to assemble into complex patterns.

To say that we find the kind of life on earth that we do because our sun emits photons of certain sizes is not a convincing argument for the presence of other kinds of life in other worlds, for so far as one can tell the kinds of molecules that are able to swallow big photons safely cannot form into chains sufficiently complex to perform the miracles of living.

Since the sun that life requires is likely to have been created at about the same time as the planet on which life is to develop, it must be far larger than the planet, so that the time interval between the cooling down of the surface of the planet and the cooling down of the sun shall be sufficient to permit evolution to take place.

Given a large star to serve as a sun, and a companion planet cool enough to serve as the abode for life, there still remain many other conditions to be fulfilled if the planet is to become a nesting place for life. The planet must not be so small that its gravitational forces cannot hold the molecules of gas it needs to form an atmosphere, or these will drift away as those of our moon have done. Again, the planet must be at the proper distance from its sun to receive energy at the gentle rate needed to induce the growth of complex molecules. The planet Mercury is so close to our own sun that atoms which might coalesce into molecular patterns there are forcibly torn apart by the heat that bumps them violently together. On Pluto and Uranus, far out in space, the sap and breath of possible life are congealed by the clammy cold, which freezes both liquid water and gaseous oxygen. But our lucky planet Earth, a fine moderate 93 million miles from our sun, receives the radiant blessings of energy at just the proper rate to induce formation of a world of plants and beasts and men.

A star which is to serve as a useful sun must be kept stable in temperature over the long aeons needed for evolution. In particular, it must not oscillate very slowly in brightness like some Cepheid variable stars, or explode like a nova. Most stars seem to be provided with a remarkable kind of automatic thermostat that keeps nuclear energy flowing steadily from their substance, as the hydrogen atoms in them combine to form helium nuclei. So nicely is the thermostat

in our sun adjusted that the sun's output of photons has remained constant to within one or two percent over the last
two billion years. Coming to life takes time, for every atomic
pattern, from the lowliest virus to the most godlike man, must
be tried and tested endlessly for survival ability. A sun that
warmed up or cooled off every thousand years by as much
as ten percent would be likely to break the thread of life
completely each time this got a start.

The thermostats with which most stars are provided, which
of course depend not on a mechanism but on physical principles, are so reliable that on the average only two stars out of
a billion get enough out of kilter to explode as supernovae in
any millennium. The last two such celestial blowups in our
own galaxy occurred in 1054 and 1604 A.D. respectively.
Any selected star has a very small probability of exploding
at any time, and we need not worry about our own gentle
sun doing this. It seems to be well enough adjusted to operate for several billion years more.

We have assumed, of course, that the to-be-habitable
planet we are discussing has been provided with an ample
supply of the various species of atoms that are capable of
gathering to form the bodies of living creatures. This condition is not difficult to fulfill, for the atoms needed are mostly
of the simpler sorts, which appear to be well scattered
throughout the matter of the universe. Carbon is especially
necessary, of course, as the only atom we know of that is
capable of building up the long organic molecular chains of
which every creature is made. With it we must also have
oxygen to carry energy in the photosynthetic cycle. Other
cycles than that involving CO_2 and O_2 are available to store
energy from the sun and carry it from creature to creature,
but none is known that is even approximately so effective.
Hydrogen also must be available in quantity, to form H_2O

molecules and serve as the great watery solvent and carrier of chemical substances to living tissues.

We assume also, of course, that most of the atoms of this new world are of isotope types that are stable, for a planet designed to support life must not be so radioactive that complex molecules will be destroyed as fast as they develop.

A gaseous atmosphere of some sort is a necessity to life on a planet, to ward off most of the dangerous cosmic rays and meteors that constantly bombard it. By far the greatest number of "shooting stars" now lose their energy and most of their matter harmlessly as they skid to flaming annihilation in the upper air. An atmosphere containing carbon dioxide and water vapor has extra value, apart from the chemical nature of the matter it contains, in that it furnishes a one-way window for energy. This window keeps the night side of the earth from cooling off so rapidly as it otherwise might. A layer of these two gases acts much like the glass in a greenhouse, letting through the short waves of light brought in by sunlight, but holding back most of the longer waves of infrared radiation that the cooler earth tries to radiate back into space. Even more important perhaps is the fact that oxygen molecules, two atoms hanging together as O_2, can gulp up the largest of the photons of ultraviolet light that come from the sun, although they sacrifice their molecule as a result. From its destruction comes the ability to form a triple-atomed ozone molecule, O_3, which can swallow very easily large photons which otherwise might get through to earth and damage living creatures.

Under this atmospheric blanket the oceans help further to keep the earth at an equable temperature, serving as gigantic warm-water bottles. Not only does a pound of water hold more heat than a pound of any other substance, but water expands when it freezes. This causes ice to float, which is fortunate indeed for life, for it opposes a tendency there would otherwise be for ponds and seas to freeze solid throughout. Thus to the wonderful wetness, chemical neutrality, and solvent action of water have been added qualities which help keep earth's summers from becoming so hot and its winters so cold that the patterns of living matter would inevitably become scrambled or starved.

To avoid falling into its sun in response to their mutual pull of gravitation, a planet must be kept revolving in an orbit, like a ball on the end of a string. But if the string of gravity held the planet in such a way that the same side always faced the sun, that side would soon become parched desert and the other side a frozen icecap. This danger is avoided by the spinning of the planet on its axis. As a result the solar warmth is distributed more uniformly about earth's equator through the mechanism of day and night. The resulting daily variation in heat and light has helped to stimulate the development of higher living forms than would otherwise have appeared. The environment best suited to bringing a creature to increased awareness is not one that remains uniform and comfortable, but one that gently stimulates adjustment to change. The first animals, indeed, probably evolved from single-celled plants that found special ways of responding to the variable stimuli of alternating periods of darkness and light.

The spin of the sun-heated earth stirs up winds in its atmosphere, and these in turn drive ocean currents strongly before them. Together these devices keep the airs and waters of the world respectively well mixed, and thus improve their uniformity in temperature and composition. It is good also that our earth spins about a polar axis not quite at right angles to the ecliptic plane in which it revolves around the sun, for from the resulting complex motion of any spot on earth relative to the sun's direction arise seasonal variations which stimulate life into new forms of endeavor, ranging from the greenery of spring to man's inclination toward ceremonials at Easter.

Is our planet the only one on which these conditions, and the many others needed to make life possible, are all fulfilled? Most astronomers at one time thought that our world was probably unique, but now, in an effort to get away from any naïveté remaining from our scientific infancy, some believe that though life probably exists on no other planet in our solar system (with the possible exception of some elementary or very antiquated vegetation on Mars), there may be, scattered throughout our visible universe, some millions of worlds on which life could perhaps develop.

4

Even on such a lucky planet as Earth only a very thin surface skin is at the proper temperature to support life. A few hundred feet below its surface the ground is appreciably warmer, and water is found to boil at the bottoms of many deep oil wells. On the other hand, the air temperature a few miles above our heads is at 70°F below zero on the hottest day, far too cold for the permanent abode of any living creature. Thus evolution has been able to progress only within a skimpy layer of earth and air and water.

The temperature of this life-supporting layer appears to have fluctuated by not more than 20°F in the last two billion years. Certainly the earth as a whole is no longer cooling off; probably less than a billion years sufficed to let it settle down to its present temperature, and it seems now to be slowly warming up. Cycles during which world temperatures vary by only a few degrees, which range in duration from a few million down to a few dozen years, produce vast effects upon the life earth carries. A change of 18°F in the over-all temperature of our planet is probably enough to account for all the climatic variations that have occurred, from the cold of the deepest glaciation to the warmest that earth has been since life developed here.

During the last two hundred years world temperatures seem to have been rising at a rate of about 3°F per century. Many meteorologists believe that this rise comes from the activities of living beings. Men now burn about two billion tons of fuel per year, and though the heat set free from this is not enough to warm the earth appreciably, the many billions of tons of carbon dioxide that result form an added curtain, which effectively shuts in much long-wave radiant heat that could otherwise escape.

During the million years of man's existence there have been four major cooling-off periods, during which glaciers slowly crept down to cover Europe and North America. Before this there were even longer periods, during the coolest parts of which the icecaps now found around the poles were spread over much of the globe. When the earth is at its warmest the icecaps at the poles melt completely, and all the oceans are filled to greater depths. Because of the melting of polar ice, the seas are now five inches fuller than they were in 1895, and the mean level of the oceans is several hundred feet higher than when the world was at its coolest. We appear now to be about two-thirds of the way up from the coolest to the warmest our planet ever gets, and the world is some five or six degrees cooler than at the warmest peak of an interglacial period.

In addition to such long-term variations in temperature of the entire earth, slow climatic changes result from drifts in the continents and growth of islands, which shift the currents of wind and water. Fossils of tropical fern and coral found above the Arctic Circle show that about two hundred fifty million years ago the countries in the Northern Hemi-

sphere were perhaps 20°F warmer on the average than they
are now, and Spitzbergen, now so bleak and dreary, was a
balmy paradise. The earth as a whole may well have been
cooler then than at present, but the ocean currents of the time
brought warmth and coziness to regions near the pole that
made plants and animals grow there luxuriantly.

Most noticeable of today's changes in climate is the warm-
ing-up of the Northern Hemisphere. For many years elderly
people have claimed that winters when they were young were
much colder in the northern United States than now, and this
belief, at first discounted as an example of what the dimming
years can do to selectivity of memory, is now found to be entirely justified. Winters in New York City have been getting
measurably milder for the past eighty years, at the rate of
3.3°F per century. The southernmost limit of permanently
frozen ground is found to be moving northward by a few
hundred feet each year in Siberia, in Alaska, and in Canada.
Some kinds of birches in Canada and Maine are dying out in
many places under the attacks of pests previously held in
check by winters of greater severity. Glaciers in Switzerland
and Alaska are receding; in fact, most of the earth's glaciers
melt now faster than they form, and can be seen to be much
shorter than they were in the past. No one can predict how
soon temperatures in North America will start down again,
so that our winters will once more become severe enough to
freeze the harbors on northeastern coasts.

The activities of human beings depend greatly on climate.
A change of as little as 5°F in the average temperature of a
region for a single season can have a much more profound
effect on its inhabitants than we commonly suppose. The
greatest civilizations have developed where temperatures were
seldom very high or low. Eskimos often barely keep alive
through the cold winters, and in tropical countries such active
work as can be done is best restricted to the cooler times of

day. In the United States a subtle effect of climate can be observed in the educational standards to which schoolchildren are held, and in their average intellectual attainment. Activity, both physical and mental, is most effective near the temperature-stabilizing sea, and falls off toward the interior regions, and from north to south as temperatures increase. Scientists and engineers will eventually be able to do much to moderate this effect, and while only small beginnings have yet been made in the air conditioning of homes and gathering places, man can expect to inhabit more effectively ever wider reaches of the earth.

5

The more highly a living creature has evolved, and the more complex any of its molecules, the more closely must its internal temperature be controlled if the chemical processes that keep it alive are to proceed at the proper rates. The many thermostats and stabilizers which our sun and earth possess give conditions uniform enough to permit the development of animals of moderate complexity, but eventually, to reach new heights of capability, these either developed in such constant-temperature baths as the sea, or learned to control their own internal temperatures with various devices.

Bees live with some success through winters that no solitary insect could withstand, by converting into body heat quantities of the chemical energy in honey, and by gathering into a compact ball in the hive and changing location in it as the outer layers of insects become dangerously cold. On hot days they air-condition the hive by spacing themselves and turning their bodies parallel so that a current of air is fanned from the beating wings of all to ventilate the hive. Warm-blooded animals have developed individual protective blankets in the forms of scales, feathers, hair, or clothing to hold in body heat, yet permit air and water vapor to penetrate freely. In addition, the higher animals have developed internal heating and cooling systems which are provided with physiological thermostats that keep their blood streams at constant temperature.

The air-conditioning system of the human body, which uses evaporating water as a cooling substance, is amazingly effective. A man lying quiet in a stifling room may lose as perspiration more than three pounds of water in an hour, to keep his blood stream near 98.6°F. When he goes out in cold weather an automatic servomechanism constricts the surface capillaries of his body so that less blood passes through them, and more must course through the deeper-lying channels where less heat will be lost. Shivering gives artificial exercise to release more energy from body fuels. Thus nature developed long ago devices which give positive control over the amount of heat the body will exchange with its surroundings.

During the ages in which their control devices were being perfected, creatures learned to find, and later to make, holes or burrows or nests for dwellings. A few feet below the surface of the ground the temperature remains about the same throughout the year, for heat travels slowly through earth and rock. The frost of winter can penetrate but a man's reach through packed soil even in a year, and the air in a closed cave lying beneath a hundred feet of rock remains equably cool for season after season.

Man has learned to use fire to warm his dwellings only in the last tenth or so of his experience. Within the past century he has learned also to provide warmth effectively from electricity. As vast quantities of nuclear energy come under his control, and he learns to harness the energy from the sun more effectively, man's managing of his thermal environment can be expected to improve at an ever-increasing rate.

Only within eighty years has the distribution of heat from a furnace become common even in American homes, and nearly half of them still lack such central heating. Although heat from nuclear reactors will warm many homes of the future, this is not likely to come from a separate nuclear furnace in each, but rather from a central power station serving a large number, from which atomic energy will be sent as heat through steampipes, or as electric power over wires.

In the northern United States many houses will continue to be heated by oil or gas, but greater numbers will be heated by electric power as this becomes cheaper and more available. At latitudes below that of New York and Denver, homes in increasing numbers will be adapted for solar heating. Architects are putting increasingly large glass areas in the newer homes, and picture windows with curtains covering the entire south side of a room are becoming common. Though solar-heating engineers conclude that it is not economically feasible at present to store heat for house-warming from summer until the days of winter when it is needed most, such storage for a day, or perhaps even a few days, can serve a useful end.

Solar-heated houses have been operated experimentally, and even in New England have been found to require only 10 or 15 percent of heat beyond that furnished by the sun. Unfortunately the special installations needed to provide this extra heat are likely to cost as much as is saved by using free solar energy instead of fuel. When air conditioning is needed, however, the unit that produces cold can also be made to furnish needed extra heat. Thus purchase of both a solar-heating and an air-conditioning installation may be justified, even though installation of a furnace and a solar-heater is not justified at present.

Air conditioning, by which is usually meant circulation of

cooling and drying air, is the most important contribution now being made to the construction of better homes. For the sake of comfort and efficiency this is needed throughout most of the summer in more than half of the United States, and at times in every part. Where the climate is very humid it is more important to extract water vapor from the air than to cool it, but the two processes go together. Though chemical reactions are known which produce cold instead of heat, scientists have not yet found a material cheap enough to cool off a house merely by the mixing of chemicals, as houses are heated by mixing carbon and oxygen. However, the heat pump, a device capable of either heating or cooling a home, or heating one part and cooling another, is on the verge of economic practicability.

The ordinary domestic refrigerator, now used in more than 93 percent of the homes in the United States in which electric power is available, depends for its action on a small heat pump. This takes heat out of the food in the refrigerated compartment and releases it in a gentle breeze of air which warms the kitchen, unless specially piped outside.

A heat pump capable of heating or cooling an entire house of moderate size must be much larger than one sufficient to operate a household refrigerator. It needs a motor of at least 5 horsepower to drive its compressor. Brine or antifreeze solution cooled by a large refrigerator is then circulated by a pump driven by another 5 horsepower motor through hundreds of feet of copper pipe, buried as deep underground as is practicable. This pipe absorbs heat from, or delivers it to, the ground, as the house needs heating or cooling. A large electric fan or blower sends air circulating across the cooling or heating sides of the unit as needed.

Heat-pump installations large enough to keep a house comfortable still cost more than a furnace using oil or gas, and to run one as cheaply as an oil furnace it is necessary to be able to buy electric power more cheaply than is now usually possible. But the clean, trouble-free operation of the heat pump makes it increasingly attractive for home-heating, and in a recent year more than sixteen hundred were installed in American homes. Most of these were in Florida, where the heating load in winter is lower and the cooling load in summer larger than elsewhere, for cheapest operation results when the two loads are about equal. However, heat-pump installations are being used as far north as Vancouver.

It undoubtedly lies within man's power to produce small changes in the general climate of a region of the earth, al-though the amounts of energy needed to do this are tremen-dous, vastly more than those released by any atomic bomb. One method suggested for changing climate has been to cover the Arctic snowfields periodically with soot, causing them to absorb more solar energy than at present and so to melt more rapidly. This would raise the levels of the oceans, and prob-ably put more water vapor into the atmosphere. Another suggestion is to build jetties to shift the Gulf Stream, so that it will warm certain coasts more than at present.

Such meddling with climate and even weather is very risky, until man knows more about the complex mechanisms of the earth's seas of air and water, and has more energy available to redress any unbalance he might cause. Even the relatively simple processes involved in the seeding of clouds to produce rain are still in a very uncertain state. We need to be able to predict the weather better before we can properly control it. Yet man can expect increasingly to be able to adjust the nest of life to what he considers the best ends. As he acts increasingly as the emissary of the gods in his control of lesser forms of life, he needs to develop mind and heart further to keep pace with the improved perfection of his hand.

Chapter Seven

The Sharpening of the Senses

The information that each of us receives about the outside world and our fellows comes in through what we call our five senses. In point of fact we have nearer two dozen senses than five. Scattered over our bodies and in them are more than half-a-dozen different types of specialized cells that are sensitive to heat or cold or pressure, or that make us feel sharp pain or dull pain, or any of a number of other sensations related to mechanical contact. In our mouths we have four separate sensory mechanisms to pick up various kinds of taste, and in our noses, for smell, a number yet unknown; in our eyes we have at least four distinct mechanisms for vision. However, many of the sensations sent from these sensors through nerve pathways to the brain are combined by it together, and it is useful to think of five main pathways of awareness. Thus the mystic sees five "windows of the soul" through which each lonely "I" within makes contact with his outside world.

As the mechanisms available to living creatures for obtaining information about their surroundings have increased in number and in sensitivity during the course of evolution, animals have grown greatly in awareness, and have tended to come increasingly alive. The lowest forms of living matter make only chemical contact with the watery world in which they live. The response mechanisms of even the most complex plants to incoming matter and energy are elementary and slow, for plants have not developed the electrical signaling systems that make animals lively and dynamic. Animals, as a result of their ability to move about, have been able to evolve increasingly precise and delicate mechanisms for picking up information, not only by sampling such molecules as may come near them, but by absorbing heat and sound and light energy as well.

Biologists can now determine with fair accuracy the stage of evolution at which each new sense began to be differentiated from those that preceded it. Sea anemones have elementary nervous systems with which they can feel and react to contact, and jellyfish have the beginnings of eyes, special spots more sensitive to light than their surrounding cells. Insects and spiders have great clusters of eyes, each an elementary microscope that gives its short-sighted owner a vague though valuable awareness of detail about objects near at hand.

Many complex animals have certain senses that humans possess in slight degree or not at all. Thus insects which fly are often helped in their aerial navigation by tiny aneroid barometers made of living cells, and by vibrating whisker-pendulums that act as turn-and-balance indicators, reliable as those on any Super-Constellation. The eyes of bees contain a built-in protractor with which they can fly in a fixed direction relative to the position of the sun as seen from the hive, and a polarizing compass that tells where the sun must be, when clouds obscure its face but not its light. Such polarizing compasses have been used by insects, birds, and even crustaceans for more than sixty million years; only twenty years ago did man first stumble on their existence and the way to make them work.

Bats, flying mostly in the dark, have developed an aid

for navigation that consists of an ultrasonar set, similar to man's recently invented radar, but operating, instead of with microwaves, with sound waves too high in pitch for man to hear. Emitting shrill ultra-squeaks, these skin-winged pilots of the dusk listen for echoes bouncing back from any obstacle ahead. Thus they avoid collisions in the dark by using a more scientific equivalent of the blind man's tapping cane.

One is impressed, in tracing the evolution of the various sensory mechanisms, by the evidence that no new window to the world was opened for any creature as an outright gift, but rather had to be slowly formed and tested by use over countless generations, as the genes in their mutations brought forward for trial all possible molecular rearrangements. No first awareness dawned in a dark and misty world when God said, "Let there be light," for light was for ages to live by, not to see by. Long after life began, some floating cells learned to show irritability, and were attracted by chemical environments of some sorts and repelled by others. They then developed elementary memories which made it possible for them to profit by chemical experience. Amoebas and paramecia, though without real sense organs, have this sensitivity to their watery environment, and are able to separate that which is good to eat from the other particles they engulf, and automatically to avoid unhealthy water.

Gradually over the ages this basic irritability developed into two senses: a more complex chemical sensitivity which still causes our eyes to water from smoke or noxious fumes, and a tactile mechanical sense to indicate contact with masses of matter. As this tactile sense became more selective, the sensing creature began to feel its surroundings as vaguely warm or cold, slippery or dry, hard or soft. By further slow stages the sense was refined to give acute awareness of surface pressures, of surface and internal pain, and sensitivity to heat and cold, to hunger and thirst pangs, and eventually also to sound and light. The chemical sense was meanwhile broadening into taste and smell, which even in humans are still closely related.

Although our various senses seem most unlike to us who reach awareness through them, the sensations of seeing, hearing, tasting, smelling, and feeling are all produced in the brain by nerve impulses that are alike. The brief successive waves of electric current that are transmitted by the nerve fibers when we smell a buttercup or see it are similar, for the sensation that results depends only on which switchboards in the brain receive the signals.

To be sure, each sensory mechanism has its own type of receptor on the body, a cell or group of cells sensitive to the impact of some special form of matter or of energy. In the retina of the eye, tiny living photocells secrete a dye, rhodopsin, that quickly fades when light falls on it, and starts a chemical reaction that produces nerve pulses. In the ear, vibrations picked up from the atmosphere by the eardrum are transmitted to appropriate nerve endings. Taste and smell in turn are stimulated by the chemical reactions produced by specific kinds of molecules on cells sensitive to them. But each sensor or group of sensors is connected to a nerve fiber that leads to a specific set of centers in the brain.

When the sensor cell is stimulated, an electrical impulse flashes from it which excites the next cell to which it is connected, and causes this, itself a tiny battery, to discharge in its turn. The pulse of current is then passed on to still another and another cell, until through an electrical bucket brigade it reaches the group of cells in the brain to which the fiber is attached, and there rings the bell of awareness. Light waves cannot stimulate the taste buds of the tongue, nor the nerve endings of the eardrum. But they do stimulate the cells in the retina, and if the resulting pulses are by improper nerve connections sent to that part of the brain which detects smells rather than sights, there is evidence that an odor may result from the stimulus of light.

All of our thoughts appear to result from the same kinds of electro-chemical pulses that convey sensory messages, and we can visualize "brain waves" sweeping across the billions of cells of our mental switchboards as the synapses open and close, switching the pulses of current here and there. The nerve cells may be likened to the protons of thought, the circuit patterns they form to its atoms, and the multiple switchboards of the brain to its molecular aggregates. All the glorious welter of color, sound, and emotional involvement of our world results from countless such pulses, and indeed all instinct and consciousness seem to be the result of their combinations. It is difficult to think of a colored mental picture as being merely a series of startings and stoppings of electrons, until we remember that the images we see from colored motion pictures and television images themselves arise merely from controlled electrical patterns.

The concept that when we see red or mauve or indigo the colors are put into the picture in our heads, has prompted some psychologists to declare that there is no color in nature, but only in our brains. This statement must be taken in the proper sense, for light waves of different lengths, bounding about from one piece of matter to another, are certainly very real, and they stimulate the brain to see color. Thus color has two aspects, as indeed do all sensations: the one physical or objective, and the other mental or subjective. Each is as real as the other, and we must never forget that all truth and reality have both their subjective and their objective sides.

Such a picture tempts some to feel that the scientist is overmechanizing his concept of nature. From the human standpoint, a beautiful sunset or lovely music are much more real than the electrical impulses, the flows of electrons from atom to atom and cell to cell, that bring them to conscious-ness. However, different aspects of reality can be seen by focusing on different levels of manifestation. A scientist has no more right to say that his analysis of a sensation on a particular sub-level of matter is the only correct one, than has the poet or mystic who focuses on an emotion or a revelation the right to say that he has found the only Truth.

2

Most information about the world outside comes to humans through the sense of sight. The feeling of contact with reality that vision brings leads us to say that "Seeing is believing," or "It suddenly dawned on me." Our appreciation of the detailed awareness that comes from sight shines forth also in such words as in*sight*, intro*spection*, and *imagi-nation*. Many more cells of the human brain are devoted to vision than to any other sense, and most human thoughts and dreams by far deal with things that have been or could be seen.

Vision is at once our most extended and most intensive means of contact with the outside world. Many eyes have looked at the moon, and some at the thousand details of a daisy, yet no one has ever touched the moon or heard the daisy's inner structure. Seeing is the one probe of our environment that can operate without the intervention of some form of matter; even sound waves require molecules to carry them.

Light waves, traveling fast and far, wing their way through empty space so freely that it is not surprising that nature has found them useful to carry sensory information over great distances. A flash of light can reach our eyes from an object 186 miles away in one-thousandth of a second, and from the distant sun, out nearly a hundred million miles in space, in only eight short minutes. But for these revealing waves we would be imprisoned in the dark, each aware only of what he could pick up through material contact or vibration. It is safe to say that light has extended man's awareness by many millionfold.

No organs in the human body are more delicately fashioned than the eyes, twin cameras ready to bring pictures to our brain of any object that reflects light as bright as a millionth that of full sunlight.. So sensitive are our retinas to those light waves we call green, some one-fifty-thousandth of an inch in length, that with them we can detect a candle shining many miles away if it sends us even a thousandth part of a trillionth of a horsepower. And so adaptable are these eyes, that simply by gathering more light with a rounded chunk of glass placed before them man has made himself aware of reaches of his universe so far away that light from them requires a billion years to cross the intervening space.

From a tablespoonful of gelatinous matter, nature has fashioned in the human eye a detecting device amazingly similar in its basic operation to the television cameras now being designed by man, yet far more elegant and precise than these. It is provided with an automatic shutter, the eyelid, and self-regulating diaphragm, the pupil. It contains a flexibly rounded lens controlled by self-adjusting servomechanisms of nerve and muscle that bend it to focus the sharpest possible image on a sensitive projection screen, the retina. In this living screen more than a million tiny photocell pickups convert the light they absorb into electro-chemical nerve pulses.

One of the mechanisms for seeing possessed by human eyes was especially developed for discerning objects in dim light. The pickups for this are connected in groups to nerve fibers, thus giving a visual mechanism more than five hundred times as sensitive as any other, but like most of today's television sets it does not record in color. When light impinges on its tiny receptors, short rod-shaped cells grouped around the edges of the retina like toadstools in a grassy field, these paint rather indistinct images, and we use them for seeing as best we can at night.

Three other sets of receptors, each sensitive to one basic color, grow more densely scattered over the central portions of the retina. These are cone-shaped cells, far better than the rods at revealing detail because each has its own nerve path to the brain, but each cell of a set responds only to light waves in the range of lengths useful to evoke the color to which its sensitivity pertains. When red receptors are stimulated through their appropriate nerve connections we see red, and so with blue and with yellow. The resulting nerve signals, combining in various proportions in the brain, produce more than one hundred thousand different sensations of hue and shade. Such color awareness, not given to every creature, brings to its possessor a vastly increased contact with the detail and beauty of the world. It is an awareness that scientists have only recently succeeded in capturing for visual memory through photography, and are but now developing for color television.

Yet for millions of years many insects, birds, and reptiles have seen in color. Biologists find in the eyes of chickens tiny colored globules of oil which serve as light filters around the minute photocells of the retina. The sensors that are to pick up only the yellow components of a color are shielded by the pigment that colors yolk of egg; the red ones are surrounded by that which is characteristic of boiled lobster shell. Some birds and reptiles possess four sets of color filters instead of the three in human eyes, and their owners may well be able to distinguish colors even more delicately than we.

Many animals see also to some extent with ultraviolet light, using waves slightly too short for human eyes to handle.

With their color- and night-vision mechanisms, our eyes are in a way like cameras loaded with two kinds of film, one suited to recording color, and the other, much more sensitive, designed for black-and-white. But the marvel of all visual marvels occurs in those animals which have the sensory pickups in their retinas on stalks, so that one set of sensors can be pushed forward when very bright light is available, while other sensitive stalks can be shoved ahead instead when faint objects are to be scrutinized. Such selective peering reminds one of a camera in which magazines can be switched from color film to black-and-white or back in an instant, but instead of being a photographic camera it is one designed for television, sending electric currents over a closed network to the brain. The important point is that nature, by her slow methods of trial and error, solved the television problem when the eye and brain were first evolved.

Having two eyes is important far beyond the safety of having a spare if one is lost. More than thirty-five million years ago certain animals whose two eyes had moved toward the front of their faces learned in their brain switchboard to fuse the images from these into a single picture giving depth, and thus achieved a better ability to gauge distances. Creatures with two eyes not so placed still look at the world in terms of one or the other of two flat and separate views and can estimate how far away something is only by swinging their heads and rolling their eyes, as cows and horses do, or by cocking their heads at two successive angles, like any parrot or robin. The stereoscopic quality that comes when the two eyes can be focused simultaneously on an object from slightly different angles was introduced into photography by the stereoscopes of the late 1890's and by the 3D motion pictures of the 1950's, but was even more important long before to our primate ancestors who, in swinging from one tree to another, for millions of years gambled their necks on their ability to judge the distance to the next branch. Rabbits of certain species have stereoscopic vision only when their eyes are focused behind their heads, for to such timid but speedy creatures accurate judgment of the distance of a pursuer has had more survival value than estimating the number of hops to the nearest sheltering copse.

We take our ability to see for granted, but its integration with our other senses must be learned. People born blind, who have achieved sight only after they are grown, often feel that they are going to bump into the things they see in a world crowding in about them. They learn but slowly to relate their visual images to what they can touch, and may never fully outgrow their first confusion. The baby reaching for the bright ball of the moon has fine fresh switching circuits in his clear new brain, ready to be engraved by experience, and no time in life quite equals the first few months of infancy for learning to utilize the sense of sight.

3

We are accustomed to feel all over our bodies such sensations as pressure and pain, and heat and cold, yet are amazed at the thought of smelling or tasting with our knees or foreheads. Yet many fishes do the equivalent of this. Sharks can be attracted from miles away by a piece of meat dragged behind a boat, and are found to have sensors scattered all over their bodies with which they do something intermediate between tasting and smelling. We taste with our mouths alone, and smell with our noses, merely because the respective types of sensors have in humans become concentrated in these locations. Not all of our senses are so concentrated;

some two hundred thousand living thermometer cells are scattered over our bodies, together with about half a million pressure-sensing cells. Buried in and over our flesh are three or four million receptor cells that give the signals which our brains interpret as pain.

Humans appear to have four kinds of taste sensors which respectively respond by giving the sensations we call sweet, sour, salty, and bitter. Each variety of sensor responds to dissolved molecules of a particular sort, and the combination of signals they send to the brain gives the integrated sensation of flavor. Acids, such as the acetic in vinegar and the citric in oranges and lemons, stimulate the sour taste buds. Various sorts of sugar molecules affect the sweet-sensing taste buds in different degrees, and so differ in sweetness; molecules of saccharin also affect these buds strongly, and only one-seven-hundredth as much is needed as of cane sugar to produce the same number of sweetness pulses per second. Metallic salts of one sort or another taste salty and bitter in various degrees. The sensation we get from any tasty food is a mixture of the four basic sensations, plus a great deal of smell, plus some feeling of texture.

In general, human sensitivity to bitterness is about ten thousand times as great per molecule as that to sweetness. This is because bitter things are often poisonous, and over the ages it has been more important for animals to avoid eating such things than to be sure of detecting every morsel of nourishing sweetness they might find.

Smell and taste are much keener in most vertebrates than they are in humans. A good measure of how aware a creature is of taste is the number of taste buds or sensors it possesses. Snakes and alligators have few, while turtles have many more. Frogs have sensors all over their bodies for tasting sour and bitter things, but apparently are quite unaware that sweetness exists in the world. To a frog sugar is literally nonsensical. Bats have only about eight hundred taste buds, all concentrated in their mouths, while cattle have as many as thirty-five thousand, with a probable sensitivity and discrimination of taste much greater than that of man, who has only about nine thousand sensory pickups for taste. Many more are scattered widely in our mouths before we are born, but by the time a man grows up he has lost nearly all except those concentrated on his tongue and soft palate.

The child who doesn't mind cod liver oil and hates spinach is not just being difficult; his taste buds respond differently from those of his mother. As a person ages, not only do his taste buds become more and more localized, but the distribution of the four types changes. At first the sweet sensors cover the insides of the cheeks, so children love candy, but as they grow older many of these pickups disappear, and the adult is then attracted by more exotic tastes, such as those of cheese and wine.

Even adults differ greatly in the way food tastes to them. The chemical *p-ethoxyphenyl thiourea* tastes bland and harmless to about one-third of all persons tested, while to the remainder it is extremely bitter. The same differences are probably found to a lesser degree in many other substances.

Closely related to the sense of taste is that of smell, which operates with pickup cells aroused by contact with many kinds of molecules that come wafted through the atmosphere. Smell is most highly developed at the insect level of life. With the smell organs on their antennae, some insects can pick up odors especially important to their lives from objects several miles away. Male moths, marked and set free as far as seven miles from a hidden cage in which a female of their species lurked, proved able to find her a respectable fraction of the time, unless the smell pickups had been removed from their antennae. They could even locate the cage from afar when smelly chemicals were released around it. However, when the female was covered with a glass jar, the males could not find her from even a second's flutter away; instead a twig on which she had previously been perched attracted them.

Bees seem attracted to flowers from a distance more by smell than by sight. The perfumes of most flowers may well have been developed as insects were first being found useful for pollination, and the characteristic odor of a blossom, such as a rose or a violet, often arises from a complex mixture of several dozen odoriferous chemicals.

Though the sense of smell was that which first caused the cerebrum or higher brain to develop, and led eventually to reason and judgment in man, smell is not now nearly so necessary to human beings as it is to most animals, and our smell sensors have been reduced to covering an area of only about two square inches in our noses. Dogs, on the other hand, have a very complex sniffing apparatus, and a large proportion of their brain area is devoted to odor. Most canine mental adventures occur in the world of smells.

Humans by and large can distinguish several thousand different odors, but to do this requires only a few types of sensors, perhaps four, working in combination. Odors have been divided by some researchers into supposedly basic components labeled fragrant, burnt, acidic, and caprylic, but biologists are still uncertain as to the exact number of varieties of smell pickups that we possess. Though human sensitivity to odors has declined in recent ages, it is still greater than that of any device man has invented for detecting chemicals, except the absorption spectroscope and the mass spectrograph. As few as a million molecules of such a smelly chemical as iodoform give an odor detectable to a human nose—so little that one ounce properly conserved would provide three million years of smelling.

As in the case of taste, people vary greatly in their sensitivity to odors. Our smell sensors tend to saturate easily, and no longer respond so sensitively to a bouquet of violets or a burning dump after the first few whiffs. Whether an odor will smell pleasant or foul is largely a matter of instinct or learning of the race, though our emotional reactions are also affected by association and experience. Our distant forebears learned to interpret as foul the odors from things likely to be dangerous to life. The matter is more complex than this, however, for many perfumes that are delectable in whiffs smell putrid when concentrated. A baby just born is said to have an odor that to its mother is divine, while a well-bathed child even up to the age of three or four is likely to smell sweet beyond telling to both its parents.

Odors have a strong emotional appeal to us because sensitivity to smell developed mainly during the period of evolution when instincts were the principal guide to conduct, before men did much thinking. This explains why perfumes and incense are so widely used in emotional procedures such as courtship and ceremonials of all sorts. Though our memories of things seen long ago are likely to pale with the years, an odor can bring back with startling clearness happenings of nearly a lifetime before. Even the mention of a perfume may bring nostalgia and the odor itself, as the poet well knew when he wrote the line: "At eve I smell the smell of mignonette."

4

Hearing was the first sense that brought awareness of the presence of energy rather than matter. Sound travels through air at seven hundred sixty miles an hour, or only one-millionth as fast as light, and its waves are long and coarse in comparison, so that it forms a rougher and less reliable probe of the surroundings.

Ants can feel vibrations that come through the ground, but have no ears to hear the fainter oscillations of the air waves. More complex creatures have developed special cells into sensitive living microphones. Air waves vibrating at from sixteen times a second to twenty thousand can set the human eardrum into motion, sending vibrations through to the inner ear, where they are sorted according to pitch by a fan of tissue containing thousands of nerve endings. Any nerve that is stimulated by waves of the pitch to which it is sensitive then sends pulses to the brain, which are interpreted there as a tone of the proper pitch. How loud a tone will sound depends on how many nerve fibers accustomed to carrying that pitch are stimulated. The third distinguishing feature of a sound, its timbre or quality, results from integration in the brain of the various stimuli heard at one time.

The threshold of awareness to the softest sounds is said to be about the same in a human being, a bird, or a catfish, if only those tones of medium pitch are considered. This is because, in creatures with highly developed hearing, nature has raised the sensitivity of the ear, at least over the middle ranges, to about the maximum permitted by the structure of the parts of which the nerve elements are made. Some humans are even bothered by head noises believed to arise from the random motions of molecules in the blood, striking nerve endings irregularly. Our belief in the great sensitivity of hearing of dogs and four-footed creatures of the wild probably arises mostly from their ability to hear higher tones than we, and from the fact that they have fewer emotions and no thoughts to distract them. Many animals, including birds, can hear frequencies far higher in pitch than the shrillest detectable by human ears. The squeaks sent out by bats for blind flying contain frequencies greater than fifty thousand vibrations a second, and the silent dog whistle shrills its commands with sounds too high in pitch for any human ear to hear.

Sound is one dimensional in that it can be contained completely, as far as an ear to hear it is concerned, in a single wavy line through time. This line represents the variations in air pressure that are to strike an eardrum. Once scientists understood this fact it became a simple problem for inventors to preserve sounds for reproduction by capturing them on a phonograph record, a magnetic tape, or any other device that can record a long wavy line. An electric current is also one dimensional, for as it flows in a wire past a given point its intensity may vary with time. Thus it is easy with an electric current to make a replica of a sound wave for transmission or amplification.

Sight, on the other hand, is essentially two dimensional, for every image covers an area. To send a picture over an electric transmission line, or on television waves, one must first unravel it into a single long thread that can be transmitted as variations of current, and then reknit this thread again, like a sweater or stocking, into a picture at the television receiver. Because of this necessity the development of television has been much more difficult than that of radio. Though one picture is "worth ten thousand words," it may take ten thousand times as many sensors to pick it up, but at least they can all work at almost the same time. The eye contains more than a million receptors for light, the ear not more than about forty thousand receptors for hearing, and a much smaller area of the human brain is devoted to sound than to sight. Nevertheless, a person with a good musical ear can distinguish thousands of different tones.

Time, which we feel to be one dimensional and to flow in one direction, is closely related to the sense of hearing and the sensation of rhythm. Playing a phonograph record backward conveys no meaning whatever, although a motion-picture film run backward makes some sense. Sound thus carries a more positive directionality than sight.

Our sensitivity to sound waves would probably have declined greatly in the days since the noises of the jungle meant life and death to our progenitors if man had not developed speech as his most direct means of communication. We produce sounds and modulate them purposefully far beyond the ability of any other animal, and our whole lives are tied up with precise, though not necessarily sensitive, listening.

Our two ears can co-operate to locate the origin of a sound. Stereophonic hearing is much less definite as a direction and distance finder than the stereoscopic vision given by two co-operating eyes, however. The re-creation of music after recording can be made very lifelike by using two separate recorded sound tracks, one to feed the proper vibrations to each ear, so that the minute differences in simultaneous pressure that reveal direction will be preserved.

Even older than our use of speech and hearing for communication of thought is the use of sound to convey and induce emotions. Music arouses feelings that reach far back into the prehistory and early culture of man. Such instruments as the lute and violin are transmitters and transformers of emotion, machines for arousing reveries and memories, and producing new emotional patterns.

Some persons have feared that the newly developed mechanical reproduction of music would lead us to be a race consisting mainly of listeners. On the contrary, personal participation in music, both that involving individual performance and "live" listening, is being greatly stimulated by the use of recorded music, of the radio, and of television. Sales of classical sheet music are booming as never before, and bands and orchestras flourish. Man's natural tendency for self-improvement, after he gets over his first stimulation by a newly mechanized art form, is beginning to re-establish the equilibrium. Increasing numbers of young people are now tiring of the more elementary forms of melody and rhythm brought by popular music, and are coming to the Haydn and Mozart stages of musical appreciation, formerly reached by a much smaller number only. Science is serving again to bring to the many opportunities previously available only to the few.

5

No longer need man depend on natural selection alone for the development, over the slow ages of evolutionary progress, of the increased awareness that brings him improved ability to control his life. Through science he can produce a vast array of new instruments that not only improve greatly those sensitivities he already has, but also open up new avenues of sensibility that he never had before. By fashioning a microscope he can look into a drop of water or blood and see organisms whose presence he did not previously suspect, though they have long caused him mysterious visits of plague. These he considered to be acts of God, not knowing that once seeing them he had the ability to dispel them.

By putting a glass disk 200 inches wide before his eye, as on Mt. Palomar, man can see two thousand times as far into the depths of space as he could with the eye unaided, and finds his universe enlarged eight billion times. Or if he wants to see into the center of a steel casting, or into the chest of an injured child, he can pick up the information on a beam of penetrating X-rays and then convert it into revealing images on a screen or photograph. Thus by extending his senses through the instruments of science, man has taken thought and added many cubits to his stature. By continuing his balanced quest he can, if he wishes, make himself infinitely more than he is today—more vital, more wise, more human.

The development in nature of mechanisms of increasing capability has always been limited by the availability of materials. Many useful devices take far too long to work out with protons and electrons by repeated trial and error. To develop wheels on living creatures would have been advantageous at many times in the past, but this problem has never been solved by nature except as man by reason has been able to bring together matter and energy previously unrelated. We fasten wheels to ourselves with automobiles, and wings with airplanes. By fastening sights and sounds on electromagnetic waves, and in colored motion pictures arranging silver atoms and color-absorbing molecules to force light waves into patterns like the original reality, we bring to emotional and mental availability happenings of far away and long ago. Similarly we have extended our sense of hearing on radio waves so that we can hear the sound of a dropped pin around the world. Now, instead of the limited thousands that used to cover a few acres around Daniel Webster or Demosthenes, all living people could, if they wished, listen together to their modern counterparts.

Many forms of energy exist which affect our lives importantly, to which human senses do not respond directly at all. It is desirable to measure and understand these. Science has already taught us, almost entirely in the years since our grandfathers went to school, how to transform many previously unknown forms of energy so that they not only can be brought into human ken, but bent to human service.

The recent application of microwaves in astronomy gives a good example of this. We have no organs to pick up these electromagnetic waves, which range in length from a few inches to a dozen yards. Though similar to light waves, they are thousands of times too long to affect our eyes. They are also too short to be detected indirectly through our ordinary radio sets. Only during World War II, when radar was being perfected, were techniques worked out to handle such waves effectively. By using them to shape electric currents, and then amplifying these strongly, scientists have learned how to observe and measure them with great refinement. Quite unexpectedly microwaves have now been found useful to plumb hitherto obscure reaches of the universe, and to reveal much about the heavens that was previously dark.

So much dust exists in interstellar space that it blots out our vision of the light from nine out of every ten or so of the stars in the Milky Way. But these stars emit microwaves as well as waves of heat and light, and especially when a great star explodes does it radiate these long waves in abundance. Having longer wings than those of light, microwaves are able to fight their way through longer reaches of cosmic dust. Happily also, clouds of atoms otherwise invisible in space are found to radiate microwaves of their own, and these can now be detected by man. Thus signals to which we were previously blind are serving to reveal undreamt-of stars through the new science of radioastronomy.

In the realm of the vastly small the story is the same. More than twenty thousand new species of protozoa have been discovered with the aid of the compound optical microscope since the first of these was built. But many of the viruses responsible for our most deadly diseases are so small that such microscopes still cannot detect them. Into this breach science has brought the electron microscope, which by sharpening vision further has made possible the saving of millions of lives, besides extending our knowledge in the domain of the molecule.

Electron microscopes, instead of using light waves, which are much too coarse for the most refined seeing, operate by picking up bulletins of information with elemental electrical bullets, the electrons themselves. With these they can produce a hundredfold sharpening of vision beyond the most powerful microscope using light. With such a device the biologist is able to see, on photographs or even directly on a fluorescent screen, objects down to one-twenty-fifth of a billionth of an inch in length, so that he can look at a cube of matter containing only a hundred atoms. The secret of life itself must be held in molecules of a size that we may thus eventually expect to be able to see, if not with the electron microscope, with some still-to-be-invented sense-sharpening device.

Some of those who fear science are afraid that amplifying the senses of man will make him not better, but merely more powerful. However, with increased awareness of his surroundings, his capabilities, and his possible destiny, man certainly can be made more alive. As his choices of action become extended, we can expect his experience, his knowledge, his understanding, and his wisdom to increase.

There are in the world, without question, other forms of energy not yet detected. Are we to close our senses to them? Or are we to follow one of man's most basic urges, and through them learn more about our universe and our place in it? More especially, are we to refrain from helping in the fashioning of a portion of this universe into more citadels for the further development of the human spirit?

To say that man should decline to enlarge the windows of his soul is as futile as saying that these windows should be rigged with blinds because what man might see could hurt him. Perhaps the blinds should not be raised too rapidly, but nature has built into us many self-stabilizing features, and to distrust our desire to come more fully into participation in our universe is to lose faith in the fruits of all that has gone before.

Chapter Eight

The Control of Information

One of the greatest triumphs of evolution is the development, during the last five hundred million years, of the electro-chemical device that has become the human brain. Whatever we may believe our minds to be, our brains are machines made of atoms and molecules, which operate with chemical and electrical energy. Scientists are now learning how to put together, though somewhat clumsily as yet, intricate electronic computing machines that can duplicate and even surpass a few of the simpler operations of the brain. This experimentation, besides providing useful new tools to make the human brain more powerful, is throwing much light on the way the brain itself may function.

We have seen that all of our sensations—seeing, hearing, and the rest—are produced in the brain by showers of sharp electric pulses sent through a network of nerves from the sensory organs. The brain is an assemblage of switchboards that correlates these signals, determining what actions the organism should take as a result of all of them taken together. To illustrate the complexity of the brain we may compare it with one of society's networks, the world's telephone system, which will soon contain one hundred million centers of communication, any one of which can be connected to any other. A human brain contains more than a hundred times as many lines as this, is provided with automatic dialing throughout, and is within limits self-repairing.

Plants, having no nervous systems, can develop no brains. The intelligence of any lower animal is found to be limited sharply by the number of cells its brain contains. Salamanders having different numbers of brain cells can be produced in the laboratory; those with more cells are found able to learn most. The brain of an ant contains only about two hundred fifty cells, while that of a bee has nearly nine hundred. In contrast, the human brain contains some thirteen billion cells.

As one might expect, a sheep's brain weighs only one-tenth as much as a man's. But weight is not the final criterion, for a whale's brain weighs twice as much as that of a man, and an elephant's three or four times as much. Nevertheless they are not more intelligent than a human, for their brain cells are not greater in number.

Although a human brain may have only a hundred million times as many cells as that of an ant, its possessor is likely to be much more than a hundred million times as intelligent, for it is the number of active connections among the cells that brings intelligence, and this can increase very rapidly as the number of cells mounts up. Furthermore, such creatures as ants and bees cannot profit much by education, for the few possible action patterns of their brain cells are well established when they are born. Practically all their brain neurons make simple automatic sets of connections with their neighbors, in the patterns which carry instinctive behavior. The experience of their species is recorded in their gene structures, molecular memories that over countless generations change only through mutations and natural selection. Many of the brain patterns of a man, on the other hand, can be modified by his own experience, and are given him as a sort of blank check when he is born, which he can fill in to draw out amounts of intelligence that depend on his own efforts.

Many of the older parts of our own brains are set in the patterns which govern the lower animals. The more flexible processes we call thought take place in the new or higher brain, the cortex of the cerebrum. When a creature loses its cerebral cortex or has this damaged, it can no longer profit by experience, for no longer has it nerve cells capable of experimenting with new connection patterns. Birds so treated can still fly, cats can spit and glower, but neither is able to learn or remember.

A typical nerve cell or neuron from the brain of a man looks under the microscope like a piece of the root end of a kelp plant. At one end it is covered with what look like numerous branching rootlets, while the other is a flexible axon or stem. This acts as a connecting wire that can make electro-chemical connection with any rootlet on a number of neighboring cells. Such contacts, the synapses, are living electrical switches. In some cases the cell has a choice of contacting any one of a thousand nearby neurons, and thousands can contact it. Thus the axon is like the plug-in jack of a telephone switchboard, and the rootlets like the connectors into which the jack can be plugged. In the parts of the brain concerned with instinct the jacks are so constructed as always to follow definite patterns of closing and opening; in parts concerned with ideas the patterns are flexible, and can be modified by learning.

The neurons and their connections in the brain of a man are like those in the brain of any other animal, but the human mental switchboards contain many times as many lines and central stations. Over the million or so years of man's existence the average size of the human skull has increased in two jumps. The oldest skulls yet found that belonged to men have room for only about 20 ounces of brain; at an inter-

mediate stage this increased to a little over two pounds. Today most men carry about three pounds of mental switchboards in their heads.

More important for human intelligence than size is the
wrinkling of the cerebral cortex, which gives increased area
for the connection patterns of flexible thought. Between
early man and intermediate man this area doubled, and it
has doubled again in modern man. We are well fixed now
as to mental circuits, for the brain of a modern man contains
many more cells than he uses effectively, and our intelligence
depends less on how many switchboards we have than on
how many we choose to leave unused in the back room.

There are in one human head about five times as many
pink or gray neurons as there are people in the world. The
more we learn to connect these in certain patterns of thought
the more do these patterns become stabilized as habitual with
us. Such repetition is a very important part of the process
of education.

Although nature has been developing the brain for more
than five hundred million years, the cerebral cortex began to
be elaborated only about one hundred million years ago, and
only within the most recent hundredth of this latter period
has the cerebrum developed sufficiently for its possessors to
be called men. Only within this time has the individual begun to emerge as important. When an ant is killed he can
be replaced by another ant exactly like him, but this is never
true of a human being. Worker ants of a given variety are
alike even to their brain patterns; because the patterns in a
man are flexible each is different, and what he becomes depends greatly on what he does with his cerebral cortex
through experience and education.

A human brain does not add cells as its possessor grows
older. In fact, the ten billion cells of each person's brain
cortex were all in place about four months before he was

born, and these are all he will ever have. Though its cells do not change in number, during a lifetime the weight of a human brain will increase about fourfold as its cells grow larger. The cerebral cortex does most of its growing after birth, and remains for years very flexible. The human infant is comparatively helpless until his brain patterns get set by learning, but this flexibility enables him to grow in knowledge and improve in behavior under a wider variety of circumstances than any other animal. An ant needs no time at all to learn to run because its patterns are pre-set; a baby monkey needs a week or two, but a human baby needs almost two years.

Psychologists do not yet understand just how we think, but they are getting a fair idea. Certainly a given brain cell can be used for many different mental images, depending on how its synapses are hooked up.

Man can improve his brain greatly through continued and extended use. He can also add vastly to its performance with supplementary devices. In the past, clay tablets, the abacus, and written and printed books have proved useful as external machines for aiding brain power. Today electronic computers, sound recorders, data-processing machines, and a thousand other devices are carrying this aid still further. No machine will ever challenge the brain as a whole, but those designed to process information can be even more important in forwarding its activities than steam, gasoline, and electric engines have been in aiding man's muscles.

2

The two simple processes, counting and calculating, can be carried out only by living creatures that think. Insects cannot count. Some birds are able to distinguish between

numbers as great as three and four. The higher animals can
do little more until one comes to man, who learned to count
on his fingers and toes, and after thousands of years could
get up to twenty. Really learning to count involves passing
the great hurdle of using numbers as abstract symbols. Once
this is done, the manipulation of numbers in addition, multiplication, and other mathematical operations can be made
automatic.

Until fairly recently forty has seemed an extremely large
number even to civilized men, and it has been widely used as a
symbol for any number too big to specify, as our parents
used millions and we now use billions. This use of forty
has come down to us through Middle Eastern civilization, so
that when we read about "Ali Baba and the *Forty* Thieves,"
or that it rained for *forty* nights, or speak of catching *forty*
winks, the number forty merely means "a great many."

How easily numbers can be handled depends on how they
are expressed. If a new name had to be assigned to each
number as far up as one ever wanted to count, as was originally the case, most people would never get above twelve
or so without counting with pebbles or dots or on their
fingers. The concept of two handfuls of fingers being another kind of unit made it convenient to handle digits in
groups of ten, so only ten basic names were needed for them.
All civilized peoples now use this decimal system. Instead of
representing the number 1492, for example, by 1492 dots,
which must be counted again every time we use them, we
represent it by four digits so arranged that the position of a
digit in the number represents the number of times the digit
is to be multiplied by ten. Thus 1492 is 2, plus 9 times 10,
plus 4 times 10 times 10, plus 1 times 10 times 10 times 10.
Such a system enables us to recognize a number quickly for
what it is, especially after we have memorized a multiplication
table of the digits, and we can tell at once where we are in

the number structure by seeing associations, such as those between ten and nine in numbers like 19, 90, 99, 109, and 999.

This Arabic system of recording numbers, with its digits and its use of position to indicate powers of ten, is a great aid to computation, as anyone knows who has tried to solve arithmetic problems with Roman numerals. Peoples who do not use this notation, if they compute at all, do so with piles of pebbles or the abacus. In this device, still widely used in China and Japan, beads representing counters are slid on wires. Modern desk calculating machines operate on the same principle, but count with the teeth of rotating gears instead of with sliding beads. The results are then displayed directly in terms of digital arrays that we can read, and the various operations are linked together mechanically instead of through the operator's fingers. In some still more modern calculators pulses of electric current are used as counters instead of beads or gear teeth, thus greatly increasing counting speed. Electronic computers are now being made that can do everything a thousand interconnected desk calculators can do at once, and do it many thousands of times faster. So valuable are they in carrying out calculations too complex to be done without them that companies wait in line for their use, and are glad to pay the two hundred fifty dollars an hour some of them cost to operate.

Opening and closing an ordinary electric switch mechanically is rather a slow way to produce electric pulses, and this method was used for counting in only the earliest electronic computers. Instead, a pair of electron tubes can be connected so that a current can be switched from flowing through one to the other and back a million times a second. This provides a very rapid yet reliable high-speed counting device. Banks of such tubes can be arranged so that any number is represented by a special pattern of tubes glowing and not glowing.

However, thousands of tubes are needed to calculate freely with large numbers in such a manner.

A simpler system of counting, in which only two digits are used instead of ten, is especially useful with calculating machines. This, the binary system, is able to dispense with all digits except o and 1. In it the number 1492, for example, is written 10,111,010,100. Here a 1 represents our ordinary 2 multiplied by itself as many times as the ordinal number of the column indicates, and o in a column represents its absence. 1492 is $2^{10} + 2^8 + 2^7 + 2^6 + 2^4 + 2^2$, so we write 1 in the 2, 4, 6, 7, 8 and 10 columns, counting to the left after the first. A 1 in the first column would represent 2^0, which is 1 also on the decimal system.

A binary number appears more complex than its decimal equivalent, but is easier to handle in an electronic computer, especially when the number is very large. If current is flowing through a tube, it reads 1; if not, o. Fifty pairs of tubes can in this way be made to express more than a million million million numbers in terms of various patterns. In the binary system only thirty-three vacuum tubes are needed to record numbers that would require one hundred in the decimal system. In fact, so great are the advantages of the binary system, despite our familiarity with the other, that most modern high-speed calculators are arranged to accept numbers written with decimal digits, translate them into binary numbers, calculate with these, and then retranslate the answer back into decimal numbers for the operator to read.

It has recently become possible to reduce the bulk of a large computing machine by using the newly developed transistors in place of vacuum tubes. They occupy less than a hundredth as much space as a tube, and use much less power. The replacement of several thousand tubes with an equal number of transistors reduced the space occupied by a special digital computer built for use in airplanes from a large room to three cubic feet, and the power needed from 2000 to 100 watts.

One electronic computer, designed especially to work out tomorrow's weather from today's atmospheric conditions, can in an hour carry out forty million arithmetical operations, handling ten thousand large numbers a second. Such a machine can solve in an hour problems much too complex for a human computer to solve in a lifetime. The closing of synapses in the brain is basically a slower operation than the switching of pulses by vacuum tubes, and millions of pulses can be sent through vacuum tube circuits while a living nerve circuit is being opened and closed only a few dozen times. Electronic computers are thus already much more rapid than human ones, in addition to being more reliable.

Though calculating machines are usually faster, a few individuals have shown a remarkable facility for rapid mental calculation. One little Hindu girl was able to multiply any two 20-digit numbers together in a fraction of a second. Neither she nor anyone else knew how she did this. Lightning calculators are usually not people of great intelligence, and it may well be that in their brains certain mental circuits are left permanently hooked up, like the banks of tubes in an electronic calculator, so that they can perform calculations well and quickly at the expense of flexibility of the brain as a whole.

The human brain, which contains apparatus equivalent to thousands of the most complex computing machines, operates on much less than 100 watts. Its compact and efficient electro-chemical switches are much tinier than any that man has tried to produce. Scientists may eventually be able to make colloidal switches as small as the cells developed by nature, but these will never duplicate or replace those used in the brain. Rather they will make possible additional useful devices to supplement it.

So great is the need of modern man for the results of complex calculations that already more people are needed to direct the calculating machines that exist than these machines have freed. Men will always be needed to supply what the machines lack—initiative and imagination.

3

Among the more important developments made by nature during evolution are devices for storing information. These help to preserve the results of experience, and thus reduce some effects of the passage of time while they enhance others. Thousands of such memory devices have been developed. Genes are nature's greatest notebook, containing as they do complete directions for putting together a long succession of living creatures.

Man has invented many memory devices of his own, and is constantly devising better ones. From the drawing of pictures he progressed to writing, a more formal and flexible method of information storage and communication. Since he cut his first memoirs in stone he has learned ever more rapidly how useful new devices to supplement his brain can be. The invention of photography was a great step forward, making it possible, through the releasing of black silver grains by light waves, to record occurrences in precise detail in a way that stimulates ideas and emotions directly. Phonograph recordings and motion pictures carry such stored information to other senses and sense combinations.

Important in addition to ability to store information is that of multiplying it so that it can be widely disseminated. The typewriter and printing press are being hard pressed as the amount of information to be stored keeps growing. Office workers in the United States use nearly two hundred billion new pieces of paper a year, and more than a trillion record sheets are said to be stored now in American business houses. In spite of the new business machines, and to some extent because of them, our clerical population is increasing at five times the rate of our total population.

The Library of Congress now holds some thirty-three million items, and as the number increases, each of these becomes more difficult to find in a reasonable time. The great space needed for a modern library has resulted in experiments with microfilm storage, and with new methods of copying and printing that will be rapid and compact. Equally important are new methods of finding information buried in a great mass.

In devising memory systems ease of accessibility must be kept in mind. Library clerks spend far too much time in finding and sorting books. Instead of having to go to a library to obtain a book, one could conceivably obtain it through a pneumatic tube merely by dialing numbers over a telephone. A further suggestion has been that of cataloguing all items of information themselves in terms of numbers, so that by dialing one could obtain any needed bit of known data over the phone from a talking record.

The game of "Twenty Questions" shows how quickly a bit of information can be isolated if the problem is attacked properly. An expert at this game very frequently can separate, from every other item of known information, even an abstract idea, by asking twenty or so questions to which the reply must be either yes or no. A relatively small number of binary digits will thus serve to designate any known item of information.

The amount of information that can be stored in a given space depends greatly on the method used. This book, together with many words that were removed from it during revision, was once stored in a pile of dictating-machine records six inches in diameter and half an inch high. In the typewritten stages it swelled in volume considerably, to shrink once more in printed form. On microfilm it could be stored in less than a cubic inch.

The storage of information on punched cards gives interesting possibilities, especially in cases where systematic separation of categories, or sorting, is needed. A clerk can sort fifty or so cards a minute, but machines are available now which can do this job more than ten times as fast. One new electronic machine is said to be able to scan five million documents an hour and separate them into any desired categories. Such a device can be of great value to large businesses, as for example the life insurance company which writes forty thousand new policies a week, and needs to change one hundred thousand or more punched cards at intervals.

Some individuals have what are called photographic memories; by merely glancing at a page of a book they can for a time read it in their mind's eye. One psychologist reported that, when a young man, he could glance over any page of one of Shakespeare's plays, and repeat it word for word hours afterwards. As he grew older he lost this gift. The mechanism that makes possible such feats of memory is not yet understood, but it could doubtless become a routine human accomplishment, unless made unnecessary by increased reliance on external memory devices. We all have both conscious and unconscious memories, and are known to remember much more than we can recall at will. What we call good memory is likely to be rather good recall, and this can be improved markedly by the conscious use of association between ideas. People differ in memory quite apart from the various other abilities of their minds, and though having a good memory is an asset, many very intelligent people have poor ones.

A modern computing machine needs one memory in which to store its results until they are read out, and another for those that are needed in later parts of its calculations. A good high-speed electronic calculator is now likely to be provided with three memories, in fact: one in which vast amounts of information can be held for a long time, which at present means that a relatively long time is required to find any needed data; one of moderate size that can be "read out" rapidly; and one that works very fast, which thus far means that it won't hold much data. These memories have been likened respectively to a library of books, a pocket memo, and a person's own mental recall system.

The first type of memory usually consists of great files of punched cards or tapes, which can be used over and over again, but can be sorted only slowly. The intermediate memory is usually a magnetic drum or some other equivalent of a set of magnetic tapes like those used in sound recording, on which sharp electric pulses can be recorded magnetically. The rapid transient memory usually consists now of an array of tiny iron rings like minature doughnuts, with electric wires passing through their holes. A thousand of these little rings arranged in a square chessboard array of wires makes a fine memory bank. When a current is passed through a given horizontal and a given vertical wire, the ring at their intersection is magnetized to represent 1, or yes. To read whether a ring says 1 or 0, a second current pulse is passed through one of the wires, which at the same time removes the magnetization of the ring. Such a ring memory matrix will hold thousands of bits of information, which can be inserted and read out in millionths of a second. In a typical hour's calculations one such matrix may be used two hundred fifty million times.

Another transient memory device whose "mind" can be changed very quickly, is the picture tube, as used in television. An array of thirty-two columns of thirty-two spots each

can be made to store as much information on the face of one
such tube, in terms of the brightness or darkness of each spot,
as could be stored in two thousand ordinary electronic tubes
used as simple decimal counters.

4

To build up any kind of unified community, from an atom
to a universe, requires communication among its parts. Hence
information, besides being processed and stored, needs to be
transferred. The stabilization and coherence of any entity,
whether an amoeba or a League of Nations, depends on the
internal transfer of reactions, and information is found to be
closely related to order.

In the orderly community of electrons and nucleons which
is an atom, basic information is passed around through electrical and magnetic pushes and pulls. Throughout the community of cells forming an animal body information is transmitted chemically, mechanically, and electrically. In main-
taining the integrity of a nation, speech and writing supplement travel and commerce. Empires such as Persia and Rome
were held together by roads along which runners could be
sent to tell the local governors what the central authority desired. All creatures that have attained the advantages of living
in colonies, such as termites, bees, and men, have been able to
do so the better as their means of communication became more
effective.

Man is instinctively gregarious, reaching out not merely
for social contacts but for unity of spirit with his fellows, for
mutual understanding and appreciation. To make him still
more human we need to increase his ability to communicate on
all levels of contact. Science has much to offer in improving
communication, whether in overcoming language difficulties

in the United Nations, in providing radar for an airplane pilot who would otherwise be lost over mountains in the fog, or in helping a patient on a psychiatrist's couch to learn to know himself better. New carriers of information now being developed are removing many of the old barriers to an orderly and united world.

Even elementary animals have ways of communicating with each other, as when the beaver slaps the water with his tail to warn of the presence of an enemy, or the roebuck stamps on the ground. Bees convey information, not only by dancing in the hive to tell the distance and direction of a source of nectar, but by passing around samples to identify the flower. They keep track of the condition of their queen by tasting a substance licked from her by nurses, and transferred to all concerned. If this material does not taste right, thus indicating that she is failing in her powers or preparing for flight, special hormones are fed to a group of larvae so that several new queens will be hatched. The strongest of these, which will emerge first from its cell, then stings the others to death. Thus bees might be said to have a language that depends on smell and taste, but it conveys only limited expressions of instinctive behavior, and not abstract ideas.

Humans have much to communicate besides ideas. We feel the need to transmit and induce emotional states, which we do informally in many ways, and formally through such expressions as music, poetry, and art. Because of their closer natural involvement in emotional affairs than men, women are especially adept at nonlingual communication, as when a look may direct a well-disciplined child to leave the room, or a kick under the bridge table rebukes a startled husband. Thus there are languages on many levels, but those most recently developed, which have knit humans into tribal and national groups, are speech and writing. Both involve deliberate symbolism that was slowly evolved by groups of people, which must be learned by each individual.

Though young chimpanzees can take care of themselves much better than human babies of equal age, a chimpanzee can never learn to talk. It can be taught to understand a few dozen words, but its brain responds only slowly to abstract symbolism. No animal other than the human can be said to have a true language which communicates ideas. Parrots and other birds that learn to speak words are not saying anything, but are merely imitating sounds for instinctive reasons.

A species of gibbon is known to make a dozen or so sounds that appear to be the beginnings of a language. Five of these mean "yes" with various degrees of emphasis, four mean "no," four are noncommittal acknowledgments that have been translated as "I heard you," and one has been rendered as "wow!" indicating emphatic pleasure. However, human babies eight months old can do an equivalent job of emotional communication with their gurgles, smiles, and tears.

Even a human baby must be taught how to talk. A group of infants tended only by mutes is said to develop a system of communication that involves pushes and slaps, gestures and grunts, and a small number of imitative sounds, but no true spoken language. Our *capacity* to speak is transmitted through the genes, but our *ability* to speak is transferred through the family and social structure.

Any of the senses could be used as a medium for a language conveying ideas, provided suitable transmitters are available when needed. Taste is a fine "language" medium for bees, but would be cumbersome for carrying human thoughts. Sending a person a box of candy expresses well a "thank you" or an "I like you," but the daily newspaper would be clumsy to peruse if, to get the news, its readers had to lick each of a hundred thousand pastilles containing assorted sour, sweet, and bitter chemicals.

A sense of touch offers a fairly good system of communi-cation, but does not operate at a distance. The first real human language, gradually invented in man's early grunting days, probably involved gestures. It would be possible to learn to say, with some three dozen of these, everything that we can now say by either speaking or writing, provided we agreed to arrange our gestures in patterns that represented billions of different ideas. Such a gesture language would not be like the sign languages used by deaf mutes, which usually involve symbols for spoken letters, but would convey ideas directly by gesture patterns. Gesture languages have not developed far because they occupy the hands, are relatively slow, and do not operate well in the dark. They are used to carry emo-tional tones which supplement the spoken language, in our experience especially by excitable Latins and Levantines. But communication by sound waves has much greater flexibility, and humans probably began to develop real spoken languages more than twenty thousand years ago.

We speak by forcing an air current with our lungs past our vocal chords, to produce a spreading beam of sound. We can control the pitch of this by tightening or loosening the vocal chords, and its loudness by the volume with which we blow. Most important, we adjust the distribution of energy among the various sound harmonics, saying "ee" or "ah" or "oh," by controlling various resonances through the operation of the cheeks, tongue, lips, and jaw, and separate the syllables by various types of clicks and hums and gasps.

For thousands of years men spoke and shouted, but were able to reach an audience only within the range of their un-aided voices. Then within a span of a few decades science brought three great devices that can carry any man's voice to any place on earth: the telephone, sound recording, and the radio. These are already exerting a profound influence on human progress, but before their fullest effect in welding world society into a more compact unit can come about, they must overcome the barrier set by the many languages that have been evolved by man.

5

A language is a great set of symbols that slowly grows by association and deliberate invention. Every human society has developed at least one language and most now have two, one spoken and one written. These change constantly, for a good language must be flexible enough to keep pace with human activity.

In the growth and decay of languages one can observe processes of evolution similar to those that occur on other levels of life. New words are created, mutate, and are selectively retained as they prove useful or not. Especially does the spoken language change. Sound is so ephemeral that a written language had to be invented to supplement each spoken one, and the two now go in pairs, the written language helping to stabilize the other. A spoken language is best for direct communication in the family, but its written counterpart is needed for carrying information across time, from one generation to others, as well as across space. It has provided an alternative system to the genes for passing on human characteristics, operating on the social level instead of the molecular.

Languages in isolated communities change rather slowly. Eskimos from Siberian and Canadian tribes which have had no contact for eight hundred years are said to be able to understand each other on sight. The language of Sardinia has changed little from ancient Latin, and Icelandic is much as it was in the days of the Vikings. On the other hand, where human affairs are active, languages change rapidly. Chaucer's

English took only three hundred years to become foreign to an uneducated Londoner. Parisian French has changed much more than Canadian French in recent centuries. Like pseudopods pushed out by an amoeba, dialects tend to form in separated valleys of a land, and where communication is slight these eventually grow into separate languages.

In America the beginnings of at least two dozen regional dialects have been identified. What is called a sack in Kansas is a bag in New York, and is likely to be a poke in Alabama. The broad communication provided by the radio and television, newspapers, magazines, and books will probably prevent these dialects from separating into distinct languages, however. In China the development of dialects went on for several thousand years without the mixing effect of good communication, so the Chinese National Assembly, like the United Nations, operates with interpreters.

There are now some three thousand different languages in the world, not counting dialects. Many of these, such as some belonging to tribes of American and African natives, are each spoken by fewer than a thousand people. The dozen greatest languages are spoken by more than fifty million people each. The three most widely spoken are English, used by about two hundred fifty million, Hindustani by one hundred sixty million, and Russian by one hundred forty million.

In these and related languages one can express any idea by arranging sounds selected from a group of only sixty or seventy into patterns of from one to ten syllables each to form words. These words are then fitted into more complex patterns, sentences, each of which is supposed to carry an idea. At first men used a single word to express a complete idea. Thus in some American Indian languages the statement "I am looking for a village" is said in several syllables hitched together, no one of which can be unhitched for use in a different context. When such a system is used, a new word must be invented and memorized for every new thought, which limits a speaker to expressing only a few thousand ideas. Since civilized man wishes to be able to express billions of ideas, a primitive language cannot serve him.

As men began to perceive relationships between ideas they produced new words by association. The Chinese written language especially shows the beginnings of this effect. Thus the Chinese ideograph for "east" is made by putting together those for "sun" and "tree," that for "light" by associating "sun" and "moon," and the ideograph for "trouble" is made by putting together "two women" under "one roof." A difficulty with this system is that it becomes clumsy when the ideas get complicated, if words rather than sounds are used as units. In such languages as English, some seventy sounds have been arranged in about half a million different words, and can be arranged into millions of new ones not yet used. These words can then be combined in any number of sentences to express trillions of ideas. With our Roman alphabet all of these words and any still to be invented can be written with twenty-six letters or less. Such a language is flexible enough to grow as men evolve, and to aid in carrying social evolution to heights far beyond the present. We perceive here the same use of patterns that appears so frequently in nature—sounds are the atoms of thought, words its molecules, sentences its cells.

When men thousands of years ago started to draw pictures on the ground and on stones, they took the first step in associating a picture with a thing. Gradually this symbolism was extended further, and conventional symbols called pictographs were used for pictures that had to be drawn often. Then ideographs came into being, each a still more conventional symbol for a thing or an idea. Thus written language, man's most valuable method of preserving and transmitting human experience, was slowly developed.

The ideographic system is still used in Chinese and Japanese writing. It is difficult to learn, because the meanings of thousands of independent symbols must be committed to memory. This clumsiness of Chinese writing has prevented a large fraction of the population from learning to read and write. As a result Chinese civilization became somewhat stagnant.

The invention that set the Western languages free to evolve further was the idea of using written characters as symbols for sounds rather than ideas. This led to the invention of the alphabet, and did for Western communication what the atomic concept did for chemistry, and the decimal system for commerce. It made possible the use of only thirty characters, arranged in various patterns, to carry all the ideas that any man has ever had.

Granted that it is desirable to have a language which everyone in the world can understand, which language is best? Three or four great languages are now competing for supremacy, with English far out in front. Half the world's newspapers are published in English, three-fourths of all mail is written in it, more than half of the radio stations broadcast it, and more than half of all scientific literature is published using it. Though one of the most difficult languages to learn because of its irregular and often illogical spelling and pronunciation, English lends itself more flexibly to the expression of new ideas than any other language.

Like trees, languages frequently need pruning. All languages can be artificially simplified and improved, but tradition makes this difficult. More than five hundred artificial languages are said to have been proposed within the last three hundred years, but none has been widely accepted. Two such synthetic languages, Esperanto and Interlingua, now war for superiority, but each has undesirable characteristics which keep it from really competing with a language that has evolved naturally.

A world language more systematic than any living language of today will doubtless arrive eventually, but it is most likely to evolve naturally through the unifying influence of the new scientific devices for communication. The desire of peoples to understand foreign motion pictures and radio and television programs should eventually bring a common tongue. Probably most people will eventually be bilingual, each using a world language plus his own, at least for a period in the world's development.

Until men possess a universal language it would be useful to have automatic translating machines, and scientists are now working on this difficult problem. Our real interest is not in how a language sounds, or how it appears in written form, but what ideas it carries. Ideas are expressed differently in various languages, and meaning is a hard thing to get hold of with a machine. However, progress is being made, and scientific papers in German can now be translated automatically into English without too much loss of meaning, if this is done using the sentence as a unit rather than the word.

6

Despite what some humanists fear about the influences of the telephone, the radio, television, and the motion picture, these new devices for communication represent important extensions of man's sight, hearing, and speech, which ultimately will result in great betterment of society. It is only their short-term influence that is worrisome. Soon they will have gone through the great ameliorating processes that result from increased human experience, and each will take its proper place in the evolution of society.

The knitting process that the telephone brings is gradually extending over the entire earth. There are now more than fifty million telephones in the United States, and it will soon be possible to connect any one of these to any of the forty million phones in other countries. Eventually it will be possible to do this merely by dialing a set of numbers. Probably not more than ten or twelve digits will be needed to call any phone on earth.

Until the present, all verbal communication across the oceans has had to be by radiotelephony. Laying of the first transoceanic telephone cable, across the Atlantic from Newfoundland to Scotland, was begun in 1955. Cables have long carried telegrams across the oceans, of course, but these were only dot and dash messages. The sounds of a voice would have been lost in the electrical caverns of the transoceanic cables. Telephone conversations had to be carried by radio, and these were somewhat at the mercy of the electrical weather.

To make possible long-distance telephony under water many difficult technical problems had to be overcome. For example, it is necessary to have an amplifier every forty miles to build up the waning words as they proceed along the underwater cable. Thus amplifiers had to be developed that could be sealed within the cable and left unattended beneath the ocean for many years. The filaments of ordinary electronic tubes burn out after a few thousand hours, so it was necessary to develop special tubes that would burn for at least twenty years of operation. Each tube put into the cable amplifiers is now tested for five thousand hours before using, to make sure that it is a healthy specimen. If one were to fail, the entire cable would be muted, and up it would have to come, at great cost. Thus it pays to put the needed seventy thousand dollars into each amplifier, which if it were required to work above water would cost only about fifty dollars.

For general visual, but one-way, communication, more American homes, with their thirty-seven million sets, now have television sets than do not. Television sales in the United

States have risen from sixty-five thousand sets in 1946 to seven and a quarter million in 1954. In 1946 the typical television set had a ten-inch screen and cost three hundred and seventy-five dollars; ten years later the twenty-one-inch standard set cost only half as much. Before long color television should be the standard type.

In all of our mass-entertainment media such as radio and television, we are suffering now from the transient conditions that arise when any new method of communication is first being tried. Much of our concern over world events, now frequently excessive, springs from the improper adjustment of the new amplifiers with which journalism is being provided by science. Our present reporting of national and world affairs resembles the period in the evolution of the radio when automatic volume-control was being developed. This was invented to make signals from distant stations as audible as those from stations nearby. Unfortunately, when no signals arrived in the set to be amplified, it built up static to the loudness of a real signal. While being tuned from one station to another a radio set would produce terrific blasts of meaningless sound. Later this defect was remedied by making the radio automatically less sensitive when no real signals were arriving to be picked up.

Newspapers today appear to use something like automatic volume control to amplify a great deal of static; the major headlines tend usually to be of the same size in a given paper, whether they read: UNITED NATIONS ADOPTS SANCTIONS AGAINST RED CHINA, or, WEST END WOMAN SHOOTS SPOUSE. If we stop reading the newspapers for a week, and get our world information from the residue of world news that remains by Sunday, the ups and downs of existence are somewhat smoothed out.

To the degree that science contributes to unworthy ends, it exerts an undesirable mastery over men. But nature spends aeons tinkering with her devices before she brings them to perfection. Surely man can be allowed a few years to get his communicating devices into working order.

In helping develop new methods for the processing of information—its storage, its dissemination, and its improvement in quality—not the least contribution of science is the determination of what information consists of. It pays scientists and engineers to work on the theory of information, especially for communication purposes, for just as milk can be shipped more cheaply by drying it to remove the water, and then adding water again at the destination, so information can be condensed for cheaper shipping. Standard birthday greeting telegrams have for some time been listed by code numbers, so that all the telegraph company has to do is to send a number representing the desired message, and an address and signature. However, the amount of information such a message can carry is just as much less than that of an ordinary telegram, as the choice of words is limited by the variety of numbers that has been set up. If this number is made too large the telegraph company eventually has as much trouble looking up the message as it would have had in sending an unconventionalized greeting.

Scientists learning to measure amounts of information in terms of the smallest number of units that can be used to convey it have broken it down into basic expressions of yes or no regarding ideas. This has led to a definition of the basic unit of information as the bit, a contraction for binary digit. Every item of information in the world can be expressed in terms of so many bits. Five bits will serve to express any letter of the English language, and about twenty-five bits any word. The ordinary decimal multiplication table that children learn contains fifteen hundred bits.

The more a creature knows, the better can it adapt itself to its environment, and its environment to its needs and desires. Information is thus one of the most important commodities of living, and its improved handling is one of man's greatest and most rewarding tasks.

We all have an inherent desire for information. This desire arises and can be partially fulfilled only because the universe is governed by order. In a disorderly and chaotic universe, one that operated by chance or whim, there would be no such thing as information. The development of life appears to be a device for concentrating order, and every creature, to remain alive, must be informed.

Chapter Nine

The Control of Action

During the past century new machines have increasingly reduced the load on men's muscles. One ton of coal, or 160 gallons of gasoline, when suitable devices to transform their energy are available, can replace the brute-force efforts of ten laborers working for a year. Now we are finding that men's nervous systems, and even portions of their minds, also can be relieved of many laborious, tedious, and repetitious tasks by the use of new kinds of machines.

There are many operations that a special machine can carry out much better than a man. Most of these jobs are of kinds that men are glad to be relieved of, if they can be sure of making a living in some other way. The number of interesting things men can do to support themselves is found to increase rather than decrease as machines take over greater portions of their routine work.

The supervisory type of machine called a servomechanism is being increasingly used to direct the operations of ordinary working machines, serving as their foremen and superintendents. This has led to the concept of a nearly automatic factory, which strikes terror in the minds of many people who see visions of widespread unemployment. Their fears, while reasonable at first sight, have little basis in fact.

It is natural for a laborer to suppose that a machine that

takes away his job will make him a starving victim of technological unemployment. But what actually happens is that a
machine almost always produces several new and more interesting jobs to replace each one it destroys.

The robot is frequently visualized as a fearsome mechanical
duplicate of man. Such monsters, fortunately, are the products of literary, not of scientific, minds. The machines of
science and technology, instead of being copies of men, are
special devices designed to supplement man's abilities. Usually they enable him to do many things he could not do before.

The earliest machines were those, such as the lever and
the wedge and the jack, that enabled men to push or pull
harder than with their unaided muscles. Then came machines
that were energetic and tireless, such as steam engines and tractors and locomotives. A bulldozer driven by a diesel engine
can now move a thousand yards of earth in a day with energy
from a dollar and sixty-nine cents' worth of petroleum fuel.
An earth-mover has been built large enough to scoop up in one
giant claw a load of earth or stone weighing 70 tons, which it
can lift 70 feet and dump 240 feet away. This type of attack
on large excavation problems is more effective from an over-
all social standpoint than processing the energy of expensive
meat and potatoes through the muscles of hundreds of day
laborers. In the days of the Egyptian pharaohs such tasks
were done by human slaves, who exemplified the evils of the
opposite of technological unemployment—nontechnological
employment.

Over the years the power of brute-force machines and of
those which do not tire has been greatly increased by improvements in motors and engines, which ever more effectively convert into mechanical work the energy released from fuels. A
typical engine of 1875, built to develop 15 horsepower for
threshing grain, weighed 7000 pounds. Nowadays this large

an engine can be made to develop five hundred times as much power for each pound of its weight.

Another important class of machines consists of those designed for some special dexterity, so that they are able to perform a repetitious task faster or better than a person can. To knit a pair of nylon stockings by hand would require nearly two months of labor, for it involves taking some two million hitches in about three miles of fine filament. Yet a modern high-speed hosiery-knitting machine can turn out a pair of nylons every three minutes for months on end. Since nylon stockings are considered important by at least half the human race, the improvement in the stocking standard-of-living that results from the operation of such a machine is not to be discounted lightly.

A second type of machine with dexterity is the steel giant that blows incandescent lamp bulbs automatically. A human glass blower, dipping up a molten blob of glass on the end of a long tube and twirling it around in the air while he puffs at intervals through the tube, can produce only twelve hundred bulbs a day. The machine, in contrast, can blow this many bulbs in one minute, twenty perfect bulbs in a second, and can keep this up day after day, as long as molten glass is fed it. Only because such a machine is able to put out thousands of bulbs an hour can incandescent lamps be sold for as little as ten or fifteen cents apiece. And the glass blower spends his time instead on ornate vases that the machine cannot make.

Still other machines are designed to do tasks that man could not perform at all without them. Airplanes and X-ray machines are examples of these. Then there are increasing numbers of machines built to carry out operations man finds too complex, too rapid, too dangerous, too expensive, or even too boring to perform himself. But the machines now causing the greatest flurry are those designed to direct the operations of other machines, the servomechanisms.

Servos are familiar to everyone, though usually not by that name. Probably the commonest example is the automatic thermostat that turns the furnace on or off to keep the temperature of a house uniform. Another is the governor used to keep an engine running at a uniform speed regardless of how much power is drawn from it. Other common servos are the tails put on windmills to turn them into the wind, the voltage regulators used to keep the batteries of cars from being overcharged on long trips, and the automatic steering engines used on ships. A servo par excellence is the automatic pilot, which can control an airplane during routine parts of a flight when the human pilots need a rest. This device can be refined, in a pinch, to take off and land a plane automatically.

The simplest servos merely give periodic instructions to the machines they control, and pay no attention to what they do. Thus punched cards have long been used to guide looms in the weaving of intricate patterns in rugs and carpets; these assume that the machine will do what it is told. More modern supervisory machines are arranged to have "feedback," a system in which the machine being directed reports constantly to the servo as to what is done. The controlling machine is then able to correct errors in the slave machine's operations before serious mistakes are made. If one tried to make an airplane fly itself by merely feeding it punched cards to tell it where to go, no allowance could be made for changes in wind or irregular buffetings of the air. A servo with feedback keeps the plane in dynamic balance, feeling out its response at every instant and restoring it to equilibrium as needed, by comparing its response with gyroscopes or other devices used as levels and compasses.

A large steamship can be steered automatically by a servo much more adequately than by an unaided man. Or, if desired, the pull of a finger on a small wheel on the bridge can be made to control the flow of power to an engine which forces the rudder to turn more surely in a storm than twenty powerful and cursing sailors could by pulling it with the largest tiller.

An improperly designed or adjusted servomechanism is likely to "hunt," oscillating about the condition it seeks to produce. Thus an automatic elevator which hunts may overshoot its floor, then stop below it, then go too high again, as if in the hands of an inexperienced operator. Such hunting can be eliminated by proper design, often merely by speeding up the control signals. Economists are coming to realize that booms and depressions are the "hunting" of an improperly adjusted servo of society.

The secret of designing a good servomechanism is to make it govern as many as possible of what are called the "derivatives" of the motion it is to supervise. A person learning to drive a car gains control over more and more derivatives. Starting with awareness of where the car is, he next learns to take into consideration the speed with which it is traveling, and the direction it is going. (Velocity is the first derivative of position.) Then he learns to estimate the rate of speeding up or slowing down of the car (the second derivative); then the rate at which this acceleration is changing (the third). Unless all of these derivatives are taken into account, the wheel will be turned in a jerky manner. Experience soon sets up better response patterns in the form of conditioned reflexes, so that as the driver learns to anticipate the car's response to the wheel, he comes to control higher and higher derivatives of its motion.

Problems involving servomechanisms have been made much easier to solve by the availability of electrical controls in cases where the servo must react rapidly or must be placed at a distance, for electric forces can be governed much more subtly than mechanical ones. As a result, the electrical controls industry is now becoming even larger than the electrical power industry, and together they are growing twice as fast as the rest of the economy. More than eight billion dollars' worth of electronic equipment is now sold each year in the United States, a thirty-two-fold increase in sales volume in only fifteen years.

2

We are likely to think of machines as being designed and built only by men, but nature has developed thousands of intricate and effective machines. Every animal body contains hundreds of them, working in amazing co-operation. Nature shows little evidence of planning her devices to a pattern, however, but rather appears, under the urging of basic forces, to try in each entity every combination of parts that can be built by putting a new atom here and a new molecule there. Those patterns which accomplish nothing useful disappear after a few generations, while those which function well are preserved by the very fact that their possessors have an advantage over their competitors.

Natural mechanisms are often superior in many ways to any that man has devised. Slow perfecting by nature over the ages has made many of its machines intricate, compact, beautifully fitted, and marvelously effective in fulfilling express functions. They are especially noteworthy because each contains provision for its automatic maintenance, for replacement of wornout parts, and for slow but dynamic improvement in performance as needed. However, man's machines are usually superior to nature's in some specialty of operation. No animal can pull as hard as a locomotive, fly as high as an airplane, flutter as fast as a crystal oscillator, or sing as intricately as a violin.

The human hand is a very complex grasping machine. It

has seven basic motions which are combined when its owner seizes an object, turns it around, moves it, or lifts it. Thirty joints must be kept under control by the balanced tensions of some fifty muscles in each hand, their motions resulting from changes in the relative contractions of the cells in these muscles as a result of signal pulses coming over nerve lines connected to them.

The owner of the hand also has an internal nerve telegraph system that sends him information continuously about where the hand is, the resistances its various parts are meeting, and how it is moving, as well as a three-dimensional television system in his eyes which helps him direct its motions. How complex the muscular movements in the hand are when it performs even the simplest operation, is realized most fully by anyone trying to design a mechanical substitute. Such robot hands are needed now to manipulate the strongly radioactive materials used in atomic piles, where chemical operations on "hot" atoms must often be performed behind glass shields as much as three feet thick. Here servomechanisms are of great assistance.

Nature has great ability, if given sufficient time, to adapt a machine to use under a wide variety of conditions. The mammals range in size from the great blue whale, which weighs 200,000 pounds, to the masked shrew, which tips the scales at only one-seventh of an ounce, yet all contain the same kind of chemical servo for controlling the production of milk. Whale and shrew are able to operate in their respective elements because of the other complex servomechanisms that have developed in special directions to fill their needs.

A remarkable similarity to the slow evolution of animals from simple to diverse forms can be seen today in the rapid evolution of mechanical vehicles. From the original motor-driven wagon have come the automobile, the truck, the motor scooter, the delivery van, and dozens of other forms needed for various purposes. We can even see the development of communication and sensory systems in vehicles, as autos blink their lights to signal for turn or stop; and of language, as their drivers give two short honks when passing, or five toots of indignation when someone cuts in. This sort of evolution differs less from the natural type than one would think, except that its rapidity in producing change results from its dependence on social rather than genetic forces.

Only some of the nerve signals that control our muscles, the equivalent of the electrical or hydraulic signals in servomechanisms, come through nerve lines leading from the conscious switchboards of the brain. Others come directly from automatic switchboards in older parts of the nervous system, which are hooked up permanently to give definite reflexes when certain stimuli occur. Such servomechanisms of nature were in many cases developed in animals early in the path of evolution, long before conscious thought was invented. Some of them operate very rapidly. Spiders, for instance, have been observed to seize an insect within one-sixty-fourth second of the time it touched a sensitive hair of the spider's body. Other insects show reaction times as short as one-three-hundredth second.

One must not let his belief in vital forces lying behind the physical world obscure the fact that the spider jumps and bites with physical devices that are machines quite as definitely as any electric motor, controlled by chemical and electric servos. Muscles are, in fact, electro-chemical motors. A typical animal servo system consists of a sensory device, such as the tip of a sensitive hair, its connection through nerve fibers to a central switchboard, and motor-control nerves which lead from this to muscles which they cause to contract or relax. Such a servo operates with a constant interplay of electrical, chemical, and mechanical forces.

The lower animals are often handicapped by the slowness with which signals can travel along their servomechanism control lines. Nerve signals in a clam, for instance, require a whole minute to travel two feet. Fortunately they don't have far to go, so a clam can close its shell and spit water fairly rapidly. As animals become more complex, the speed of transmission of nerve signals increases rapidly. In a crab they travel from brain to muscle at about 600 feet a minute, in a frog about seven times as fast, and in a human being at 24,000 feet a minute. Because the human body contains nerves that can carry impulses ten thousand times as fast as those of a clam, it can be a larger, more active, and much more complex machine.

This increase in the speed of nerve signals with evolutionary status does not seem to square with what we know of the very rapid motions of insects. Insects are small, however, so their nerve impulses have very short distances to travel, and they are controlled through less intricate circuits. Speed of response can also be improved by using larger bundles of nerve fibers. One of the largest bundles of nerves biologists have found is that possessed by the giant squid. When this animal senses the approach of an enemy it sends to its engine room through this motor nerve a flurry of electrical pulses which cause giant muscle cells to contract, opening wide the throttles on a strong jet-propulsion motor that shoots its owner ahead with all possible speed.

The actions that humans perform as a result of conscious thought are much slower than their reflex actions, in which nerve switches are closed automatically. Such familiar reflexes as the knee jerk are controlled in the old brain, trained through millions of years of practice to activate the needed nerve circuits automatically. If conscious thought is required, the complex new brain is involved, and the selection of nerve circuits to be closed takes more time. This can be demonstrated by the old trick of letting someone hold his thumb and fingers opposed across the center of an up-ended five-dollar bill, ready to snap closed on it as soon as it is dropped. If he must pay five dollars whenever the bill slips through his grasp, in order to win the bill whenever he can take it without moving his hand to follow its fall, this is a losing proposition. The bill will fall from between his fingers in one-eighth second, but one-seventh second is required for the necessary impulses to travel from his eye to his brain to his fingers. Anyone able to respond by reflex action would win, however. A person requires at least one-seventh second to wink his eye on purpose, but when a pebble or an insect comes toward it, the eyelid drops automatically in a third of this time.

The pupil of the eye is made to contract by a nerve servo whenever light shining on it increases in brightness. Impulses from the optic nerve go to the old brain and there cause a set of switches to be closed so that signals will be sent to a motor system that contracts muscles around the pupil of the eye. This happens even when its owner cannot think, whether because he is asleep, or drugged, or is an animal without a higher brain.

3

One of nature's outstanding mechanical achievements is the development of devices that can fly. The smaller a creature is, the more easily can it be made airborne; bacteria do not even need wings to keep them floating in the air for days. After concluding many times that flight for a body as large and heavy as his own was impossible, man finally succeeded in flying, and in launching on wings much heavier loads than his body. In fact, man's improved control of energy has resulted in his being able to fly the equivalent of a locomotive with wings, at speeds faster than sound. Airplanes can now fly higher, faster and farther than any bird.

Yet how much more meticulously fashioned is the bird, and how delicately controlled! The plane has only a few sets of air surfaces that can be adjusted to maintain its balance, while the bird has hundreds. In fact, because nature has learned the value of being profuse with servomechanisms, most birds have separate bundles of nerves and muscles to control each individual feather of hundreds.

The problem of flight has been solved by nature, through independent lines of development, many separate times. Of those types of fliers that have survived, among the best are the smaller insects, which for millions of years have been buzzing about on real wings made of gauzy plastic. All the other known fliers are quadrupeds, far higher in the scale of evolution, which use wings that were gradually developed by modifying two of their four limbs. Bats developed wings from their hands by growing skin between their elongated fingers. The pterodactyls, large lizards now extinct, learned to fly with their little fingers as these gradually developed into flapping wings. Still only part way along their path of evolution into fliers, and hence only fair performers in the air, are the flying squirrels and the flying fish, already expert at parachuting and fluttering respectively.

Birds are the most impressive flying machines, for with their wings nature has learned to support on molecules of air bodies weighing a dozen pounds or more. The great flying ability of a bird comes mainly from the successful development of the feather, one of the lightest mechanisms of its strength that is known. A wing feather may have more than twenty million separate segments, held together by hundreds of millions of tiny hooks which form little zippers that produce a gauzy net through which molecules of air can find their way but slowly. These zippers are self-repairing; when a bird smooths its ruffled feathers it is pushing their seams to lie parallel so that they will zip together again.

Since the feathers with which a bird flies are dead, they cannot be kept in repair by nature's usual methods. Instead, a new feather is grown in the moulting season to replace each old one, whether worn out or not. So that the bird can still fly straight while losing feathers, these fall out evenly from the wings on each side.

Birds have had to make many sacrifices to attain the gift of flight. Many have given up their sweat glands to save weight. Female birds have only one ovary instead of two, thus trading security of reproduction for the sake of easier flying. During the nonbreeding season the sex organs of both male and female birds diminish greatly in size and weight. To achieve better balance, the heads of birds have grown light relative to their bodies, and they have lost their teeth. In place of these they use gravel in their gizzards for grinding food, to concentrate weight nearer the center of balance. To operate their wings birds have had to develop unusually strong breast muscles, fed energy by a powerful heart. To speed up the release of this energy from food their body thermostats have been set high. Most important, birds have probably traded for flying ability their chance ever to become as intelligent as animals in other branches of the tree of evolution. When their forelegs grew into wings they lost the chance of ever having hands, and so have had to gather food by pecking at it with the face. Thus they lost the relative isolation of the main sensors collected in the front of the head, an isolation which led ultimately in the primates to the encouragement of contemplation.

The framework of an avian flying machine shows well nature's automatic methods of achieving perfection. Great frigate birds with wings that spread over seven feet are constructed on rigid frames of bones weighing only a few ounces all together, less than the feathers that clothe them. Birds' bones are usually hollow, and in some cases are even internally air-cooled. Nature's methods of strut design, though extremely slow, have achieved remarkable results. When the inside of one of the wing bones of a large bird is looked at through a microscope, the most intricate triangular trusses can be seen. These stiffen tapered spars and fared and rounded joints.

Not only has nature developed patterns over the ages which give to bones great strength combined with lightness, but she has perfected a mechanism whereby improvement and strengthening automatically take place as needed. In response to undesirable bending of a bone a chemical demand is set up, and cells stiffened with calcium are laid down where the stresses are greatest. Thus the cells possess an automatic mechanism for plotting out the contours of strain. It is as if an engineer, building a bridge across a river, could arrange for molecules to deposit themselves in those parts of girders where the danger of breaking was greatest, and to leave any locations where weight was greater than that needed for strength. This observation of nature's methods of achieving perfection should give comfort to those who fear for man's spiritual progress, for there is much evidence of the same perfecting principles guiding the servomechanisms of the soul.

Many heavy birds such as ducks and geese have trouble launching themselves into the air. Some are said to need five times as much energy while taking off as they need to keep flying a level course. However, their ancestors have learned to take off against the wind, get a good running start, and push against water with their feet and tails when possible. These successful tricks are built into their patterns of reflex action and appear as instincts.

A bird's wings combine two purposes: they support him in the air, and they propel him forward. In the airplane the mechanism of propulsion has been separated from that of support. This makes possible great improvements in the efficiency of each. Their degree of specialization is shown in the great differences in appearance between the propellers of a modern airplane and its wings.

In only fifty years man has brought the airplane to the stage where it can do many things better than birds, especially in flying fast and far. Until jet engines were invented the speed of a plane was limited by the need for the tips of its propellers to move faster than the plane itself. This required excessive power as the speed of sound was approached. However, in the range of speeds in which the efficiency of propellers is falling, that of jets is rising. Although jet planes are not yet as safe as propeller-driven planes, they can be made so. Nuclear power will undoubtedly become increasingly important for plane propulsion once methods are developed for keeping harmful radiations away from pilots and passengers.

The brute force problems of overcoming lift and drag in airplanes are well on the way to being solved. Now great stress is being laid on the development of servos to refine their controls. One great such advance was the introduction of the variable-pitch propeller. When it became possible to twist the blades of a propeller in midair without stopping it, servomechanisms were arranged to seek automatically the most effective angle for slicing the air under the conditions existing at any moment. When increased pull is needed, as when the plane starts to climb, the blades under servo control take deeper bites of air.

The pilot can also vary the pitch of the propeller by hand. He can feather the blades so a propeller does not pull at all, if its engine should need to be stopped because something has gone wrong with it. On landing, the pilot can reverse the blades so the propellers push back against the coasting plane, thus braking its motion without danger of skidding.

The control muscles of a big airliner are combinations of electric motors and pumps which circulate oil at high pressure to hydraulic plungers, which can be made to exert forces of many tons. The landing gear of a large modern plane, in an emergency, takes several men fifteen minutes to crank up by hand; ordinarily a strong hydraulic servo makes it possible for the pilot to retract the gear in fifteen seconds merely by pressing a button.

Planes are also being given new sensory devices. Pickups resembling large nerve receptors are used in large planes to watch the pressure cycles in the cylinders of each engine during flight. The plane engineer can then observe if every spark plug is firing, and whether the explosion cycle is normal or not. He also has devices which constantly measure vibration. Any of these sensors can be made to ring bells or flash lights when something goes wrong, so that an engine can be turned off before further damage occurs, and perhaps repaired.

Airplanes are thus rapidly being given the equivalent of automatic and of conditioned-reflex nervous systems. As the calculating devices used in a plane's operation and navigation are made more automatic they take on the character of parts of an incipient mechanical brain. So complex is the array of instruments in the pilot's cabin becoming that synthesizing machines have had to be developed, like those developed long ago in animals. For instance, a single throttle is now arranged to take care of seven different adjustments for controlling each engine of a DC7 or a Super-Constellation, as the plane settles smoothly to the task of riding on untold trillions of air molecules, with energy released from lesser trillions of gasoline molecules.

4

It is possible to build machines that can learn, and learn in a very real sense, though the memories they are given are more like those of instinct than those of thought. A mechanical mouse built by Dr. Claude Shannon of the Bell Telephone Laboratories learns amazingly quickly. This tinny creature is put into a complex little maze, which can be set up in any desired shape while the mouse is out of the room. The first time it is sent through the maze the mouse makes mistakes at almost every turn, bumping into walls and trying every possible direction until it finally gets through the maze and rings a bell at the end. The second time the mouse is put into the maze, however, it makes every turn correctly, and goes whizzing through to ring the bell in less than a third of the time it required before.

This remarkable learning ability depends on electrical contacts and relays. The mouse is driven by a tiny electric motor, arranged to push it straight ahead until it hits a wall. Such an impact causes it to turn sharp right, and then it goes straight ahead until it hits another wall, when it turns again. Thus the mouse is propelled successively in each direction, except that from which it has come, until it bumps into a wall. One direction out of three will always turn out to be correct in any single decision, no matter how the maze is set up.

The reason the mouse makes no mistakes the second time through the maze is that the act of hitting a wall the first time through closes a switch which prevents it from trying that direction the next time through. The various switches underneath the maze are thus set, by the very bumps of the first experience, in a correct pattern to lead the mouse through. All creatures probably learn in a similar way, but their adventures are much more complex so they need many bumps before a given lesson is learned. But one lesson may teach many things, so the more highly evolved a creature becomes, the fewer actual bumps is it likely to require to set its response patterns straight.

A good example of a machine that is still evolving rapidly, as new characteristics are built into it, is the modern elevator. Without electrically controlled elevators we could not have modern office buildings. In 1889, a person wishing to be carried up the Eiffel Tower had to change elevators three times, making the 1000-foot ascent in four separate hydraulic lifts. In the early 1900's elevator accidents were very common. In a single large city it was not unusual for as many as thirty people to be killed in elevator accidents in one year. In fact, more people were being killed in elevators fifty years ago than are being killed in airplanes today.

Electric motors now usually do the actual work of lifting an elevator, and a "nervous system" of electrical circuits is used to control servomechanisms designed to give it the semblance of elementary memory, discrimination, and judgment. It was comparatively simple to furnish an elevator with switches that would permit it to be operated only when its doors were closed, and to allow its doors to open only when at a floor. Then a sort of automatic nervous system involving servos was developed, to stop it level with any floor, and to open its doors automatically. But this was not enough, for an automatic elevator is likely to get conflicting orders from would-be users who summon it to different floors at the same time, and if blindly obedient can be expected to forsake the errand set by its first passenger, in response to every later buzz. To offset this, electrical relays were arranged so that once the elevator starts for a floor to which it has been called, it will ignore any call except one to a floor on the way to its destination.

Then elevators were given memories with electrical switches and relays arranged to store information. Where they are operated in groups, each can then be told what the others are doing, and circuits can be arranged to decide what each elevator should best do next. A fine modern bank of elevators can make the best possible sense out of all the commands that come to it, without being panicked by unreasonable demands from any passenger. Thus elevators are gradually being given judgment in a manner reminiscent of the development of the brain in lower animals.

An example of a machine that contains a servomechanism which can be adjusted to various degrees of external control, or made more automatic, is a new type of iron lung. The ordinary iron lung expands and contracts the lungs of a patient whose breath-control nerves are incapacitated, taking on the jobs of some of his muscles and the nerves connected to them as well. In so doing, it may take away the very stimulus that is needed by the patient to get his own muscles into action again. The cybernetics engineer, an expert in control devices, can in the new type of iron lung connect electronic apparatus so that the machine will carry out the breathing effort as needed, but leave to the patient as much control as it is good for him to take at any time. Thus he is induced to exercise such nerve paths as still remain functioning. By adjusting control knobs the physician can make the patient take on a gradually increasing fraction of the effort of natural breathing, until his nerve and muscle action is re-established as close to normal as possible.

Many operations too delicate for human hands can be carried out with self-controlling servos of the same type as are used in guided missiles for so-called "push button" warfare. For example, a biologist may want to extract the nucleus from a microscopic living cell with a tiny hollow needle. A servo could be used to pick up photoelectrically the magnified image of the tiny nucleus, and through electronic signals unerringly guide the minute suction tube to its proper position to finish the job.

Automatic machines are bringing about a revolution in human affairs which may become even more important than that which resulted when the printing press became available to make millions of copies of stored mental images and ideas. One typewriter can be made to operate thousands of others in as many cities. A master metal-cutting machine can be made to control others like itself which produce many duplicate machine parts at once. Automobile engines, for example, can be made with automatic milling machines which turn out hundreds of identical engine blocks from solid steel, their motions guided to closer than a thousandth of an inch by a master machine which takes its orders from cams, or tables of typewritten numbers, or tapes punched with coding holes, or magnetic tapes, or even from wooden models carved from designs modeled in clay.

Fears that lathe and milling machine operators will be thrown out of work as a result of such machines seem largely unfounded, for the same reason that more printers are employed today to run the world's presses than when all the type had to be set by hand. Mechanics will always be needed to supervise the machines, and to provide imagination and greater flexibility of control than a machine can give.

5

The great bogeyman of the machine age is technological unemployment. Like most bogeymen, this one can be seen only when looked at in a dim light. Machines make many more new jobs than they destroy, and while it sometimes takes a little time for these new jobs to develop, in an expanding economy even the temporary dislocations sometimes produced by automation are seldom apparent. To make an economy expand there is nothing better than useful new machines. Between 1940 and 1955, the period of most rapid introduction of automatic machinery that we have yet seen in the United States, the number of available jobs increased by more than 35 percent.

When a worker operates a machine which greatly increases his output, his employer can afford to pay him more. Especially is this true when the employer can sell a better product for less, thus expanding the market. The buyer then gets more for his money, so he can afford to buy more products. This virtuous circle causes the economy to expand. Many new jobs then result from the opportunities which arise for filling more human needs, which grow in numbers as man's imagination expands.

There were twenty-nine million jobs in the United States in 1900; by 1953 this number had grown to sixty-six million, of which about twenty million were filled by women. Employment has been going up most rapidly in those industries in which automation has been most actively introduced. The telephone system of the United States is being made automatic as rapidly as possible, so that it will be possible to reach any phone anywhere by dialing from any other. This practice could be expected to put operators out of work, yet the telephone company keeps advertising for more, so that the numbers of operators increased by 159,000, or 79 percent, between 1940 and 1950, in spite of automation.

Automation has also been spreading widely in the automobile industry. It has been estimated that a modern automobile, if built by hand with the methods of fifty years ago, would cost more than sixty-five thousand dollars. The difference between sixty-five thousand dollars and three thousand dollars is to some extent a measure of the advantages of machines in producing automobiles. During the years in which automation was being introduced the number of automobile workers has doubled.

A great industrialist and a great labor leader have announced independently that they knew of no case where technological advances have thrown people out of work. Between 1914 and 1947 the manufacturing output of the United States increased by 161 percent, while the real wages of workers, measured in purchasing power, increased by 157 percent. The prices of manufactured products, measured in terms of hourly wages, increased by only 61 percent.

Such unemployment as occasionally exists today is likely to arise from a lack of adaptability in the individual, or from a static or falling economy. The senator who once objected to the use of steam shovels in digging a canal because he had so many pick-and-shovel laborers among his constituents, probably did not appreciate the suggestion of another senator that teaspoons be used so that still more jobs would be created. Unemployment comes primarily from clogging the wheels of commerce, and new machines help to keep these unclogged. Their greatest effect is to increase over-all prosperity.

The greatest direct effect of new machines on labor, after the increased pay they make possible, comes from the fact that they produce so many new jobs that it becomes increasingly difficult to fill the more commonplace jobs that existed before. We can blame on the increased numbers of good industrial jobs that are produced by machines the fact that painters, plumbers, bricklayers, parlor maids, cooks and nurses are now becoming embarrassingly scarce, and we must have recourse to "Do It Yourself" programs.

Over the last one hundred fifty years the productivity of labor has been increased at least fourfold by scientific development. As a result, the living standard of the average family has more than doubled in each generation. Is this good from the standpoint of the humanist? Was a man who had to work fourteen hours a day to afford a shack in which he could live on dark bread and soup better off than a worker of today, who by spending only half as much time at work can have a comfortable home, a well-nourished family, and an opportunity for as much education as he and his children can absorb?

Society has become able to afford such luxuries as forbidding children to work long hours in sweatshops at uninteresting jobs only as a result of the technology that has sprung from science. Far from enslaving man, the machine increasingly gives him a choice as to what he shall do. In terms of the things human beings in general desire—better health, longer life, greater security and comfort, increased opportunity for enlightenment and spiritual development, and more effective communication with their fellows on all levels—science has made life in the 1950's far better than that of the 1850's. Nor is the man of today demonstrably less spiritual than his predecessors of a century ago. In fact, he is likely to be more friendly, more tolerant, and more charitable than his great-grandfather.

As to the likelihood that increasing dependence on machines will reduce man to the role of a dispirited and dull observer at the mercy of his robots, losing his ambition, his energy, and his interest in living, I fail to see even beginning signs of this. There is surely more boredom among a thousand Oriental peasants carrying water in buckets, or ineffectively pumping it by walking on treadmills, than among a thousand American farmers buying gasoline to run irrigation pumps. Worry over mechanization springs from a lack of proper assessment, not only of the role of science in human affairs, but of the characteristics of men. The evidence is overwhelming that man's material achievements can and, because of his nature, will in the long run contribute greatly to his spiritual welfare. Without them, as the study of both history and nature shows, he could not reach the full flower of his capabilities.

Men of heart, with minds and spirits, need fear no machine; to them science opens up an endless frontier of opportunity. Humanists may disavow the wealth technology brings as an end in itself, but as a means to the ultimate spiritual ends of humanity they disavow it at their peril.

Chapter Ten

The Human Personality

Man is gradually coming to realize that he is inwardly not quite so simple a creature as he has felt himself in his own mind to be. Each of us is likely to think of his conscious mind as his real self, but we are acquainted with only a small part of our own personalities. We all have "hidden depths," and the greatest extent of these depths is not exposed. We are driven by many instinctive behavior patterns over which we may have little conscious control, and by strong emotions and forces of desire. We have inner unconscious memories of which we are scarcely aware. We have higher drives such as curiosity and aesthetic sensibilities. Crowning all we have consciences and loyalties and aspirations and reverence.

People differ in more ways than we are likely to appreciate offhand. We can see their differences in height and weight and appearance. Each is unique in his spoken voice, his handwriting, his use of language, his genes, his fingerprints, his blood type, and many of the kinds of protein molecules his body contains. People differ greatly also in their sensitivity to the various sensations, in their reactions to pain, in memory, in learning ability, in reaction times, in general intelligence, and in hundreds of other ways. Unlike ants or bees or maple trees, all of which are pretty much alike in a species, each human has a different personality.

One of the greatest developments of evolution has been
the emergence of the human individual as an important and
unique being in his own right, rather than as a member of
a swarm of similar beings. Though all of us would appear
superficially alike to a man from Mars, we differ in ways
that are sometimes even more important than our resemblances. Humanity makes progress by using these individual
differences to produce changes in the most advantageous direction for further evolution.

It is convenient, though somewhat artificial, to think of
the mind as containing three sections, which can be related
roughly to three different collections of switchboards in the
brain. Oversimplified, these may be thought of as the seats
of reason, of desire, and of conscience, respectively. Freud
called the conscious portion of the mind in which thought
images occur the ego. The great unconscious part of the
mind, filled with urges and desires and drives, he called the id.
Finally he called the superego that part of the mind in which
are stored traditions, taboos, moral precepts, and other results
of racial experience.

Much of our occasionally amazing behavior becomes more
understandable in the terms psychologists now use to describe the mind. Its division into parts, however, is merely
for convenience of description. It would be as difficult and
nonrevealing to describe the mind in terms of the millions of
kinds of switchboards for nerve currents it contains, as to describe a piano in terms of the particles of wood, felt, and
steel of which it is composed.

The ego, or conscious mind, is the seat of thought, reason,
and visualization, and is the front assembly room of the
imagination. It superficially controls the personality during
the waking hours, constantly driven by the id, and restrained
by the superego. The id can be likened to the devil shouting
in one ear, while the superego is the voice of conscience

whispering in the other. These two correspond to the lower and upper selves with which mystics have long been concerned.

In sleep the ego loses much of its control over the personality, parts of the superego are somewhat suppressed, and the id is able to play up its instinctive desires with loosened censorship. Dreams are often messages in code that the id is sending up to the small residue of the conscious that remains active during sleep. The strange behavior of a human following the dictates of the subconscious mind as controlled by suggestion are strikingly revealed when we see a person, especially one with whom we are well acquainted, in a hypnotic trance. Then control by the conscious mind is removed or greatly diminished, and the subconscious is controlled instead by the dictates of the hypnotist.

A good personality can be thought of as one in which a proper balance exists among the body and the various parts of the mind. Success in achieving this balance is measured in terms of the state called happiness. From the standpoint of the individual, the objective of all human behavior is happiness, but happiness is difficult to plan for except on a statistical basis.

Often the objectives of nature and those of the individual conflict. Happiness appears to result from the satisfaction of urges, coupled with freedom from fear, anxiety, and frustration, plus awareness of beauty, plus a feeling of creation and achievement. These are frequently in conflict, one course of action resulting in immediate happiness and long-term suffering, and another giving the opposite result. Though maximum integrated happiness can be attained most readily by a personality in balance, the race makes most of its progress as a result of the activities of geniuses, who are usually somewhat unbalanced, or rather, overbalanced, personalities.

Although science is mainly occupied with the conscious

mind and the development of reason and imagination, these alone are not enough for man's happiness. His needs are not filled without a proper balance of physical, emotional, mental, and spiritual activity. Besides his strong urge of curiosity he has an aesthetic urge toward beauty, and a mystical urge toward religion. Our methods of education, somewhat deficient in the production of reason and perhaps overly emphasizing tradition, need to guide each human being toward the balancing of all aspects of his personality.

Reason, that function of the conscious mind most directly affected by science, helps us to proceed directly from causes to effects, and to relate human experience of the past to that of the present and the future. Other attributes of consciousness are prudence, expediency, common sense, and imagination, which together with reason make up intelligence. Intelligence helps man to put on the snowshoes of experience. These reduce in magnitude the ups and downs that time and experience bring, by making it possible for him to live in the past, the present, and to some extent the future at the same time. This greatly increases his survival value, for he can avoid mistakes that previously would have been fatal.

Those parts of the brain of man which are much more complex than those of any other animal are the ones concerned with memory, with such symbolism as speaking, writing, and understanding, with the solving of problems, and with the projection of images. All sorts of new mental adventures are made possible by the development in man's higher brain centers of new mutual associations among great groupings of nerve switchboards.

All of our thoughts and mental processes are end-products of switching patterns and nerve circuits, and in the brains of the higher animals these have become capable of internal stimulation, rather than always requiring a stimulus from the external world. As a result man has developed the ability to see within his brain images which can produce in him reactions as effective as if caused by an actual sound or smell or visual image. As a result we can supplement sensation with thought, and can profit from a much larger number of experiences than we could possibly undergo in actuality, for many of these now need only occur within our minds. Again nature has evolved something new from the profitable cooperation of lesser elements.

By substituting for immediate sensations mental images of things, whether we have previously sensed them or not, we can perform all sorts of interesting mental experiments. Thus Newton, his senses stimulated by an apple, thought not merely of apples but of planets, and had no need of a space ship to work out his Law of Universal Gravitation.

Animals low in the scale of evolution do not possess the ability to carry the outer world into their minds, and reproduce parts of it at will. Humans can close their eyes and see mental images, not only of things they have seen in the past, but of things they have never seen. This enables men to repeat their own experiences over and over for digestion into wisdom, to visualize and benefit by the experiences of others, and to learn from experiences that might occur but need not. Some kinds of things we can learn only through personal experience, but our ability to be educated by simulated rather than actual experience measures the degree to which we can avoid much suffering through mistakes of judgment.

2

The philosopher Hume defined mind as an abstract term denoting a series of ideas, memories and feelings, which appear in consciousness, and so overlap that they give the impression of being continuous. This sort of definition has been the basis of statements that mind is an illusion. But in the same sense matter is an illusion also, for it consists mostly of empty space, and its apparent hardness and permanence result merely because we feel and observe it with fingers and eyes composed of the same tenuous matter.

All of the higher animals possessing cerebral hemispheres apparently share our sense of individuality, or "I-ness." Many psychologists call this feeling that each of us is the same person day after day illusory. However, the word illusion must be taken for what it is; it serves mainly to keep us thinking straight, so that we will not read more into the mind than is there. In point of fact, the surest thing that each of us knows appears to be that "I am I," and according to one school of philosophers this is where all real truth begins. Descartes' most famous dictum was, "I think, therefore I am." There are good reasons, however, why many biologists do not like to talk about mind at all, but speak rather of consciousness, and think of this as analogous to a series of images projected on a moving picture screen. The usefulness of such an image depends on the level from which an observation is to be made.

Consciousness hooks up the past to the present for each of us. It has been defined as "awareness of the environment and of the self, which has the ability to make a choice between a number of courses of action, and relates past experience to what it anticipates in the future." Consciousness may well result from a series of very short stimuli, of either internal or external origin, that produce pulsations in the nervous system, so that we may be thought of as observers of a motion picture or television screen. Since it takes time for each sensation to be felt, successive ones overlap, and we have the impression of continuity. But when one gets to this philosophical level he is beginning to reason about the meaning of reality, which we must postpone to the final chapter.

We subjectively feel that we are conscious when awake, and unconscious when asleep, but actually there are many degrees of consciousness or awareness. The ant, the bee, the crab, the octopus, and the frog, all have awareness in increasing degrees. A cat is much less conscious than a man. Consciousness produces an integration that may result in action, and can be measured in terms of results. The switchboard that is the gate of consciousness in higher animals is now believed to be in the diencephalon, a part of the brain below the cerebral cortex.

Our brain is still in process of evolution, and we are learning to comprehend the limitations of our ways of thought. Our ideas tend to gather into closed rings that tend to remain fixed and unaltered; when one of these rings snaps shut we have a closed mind insofar as the ideas it comprises are concerned, and feel well satisfied, self-righteous, and willing to defend our views against all comers. Contact with reality causes these mental patterns to be shaken loose, so that rings of small radius are combined into larger rings that cover a wider range of facts. When we keep our mental patterns closed and small in radius, we are more complacent and comfortable, but as they grow we become more intelligent, aware, alive, and able to react more properly to our environment. Therefore it is to our advantage to keep them flexible by education and lubricated by emotion, so that we can enlarge them to the greatest degree possible. We are not mentally at ease, however, except when our mind patterns close once again into their stable configurations, like electrons forming stable atoms.

3

Much human activity is still the result of emotional forces arising in the old brain rather than of intellectual forces arising in the new. The two constantly strive for control of each personality, each social group, each nation, and the world. When a proper solution to a problem is found, both emotional and rational needs are likely to be satisfied. A person governed entirely by emotion has poor survival value, while one governed purely by intellect would have little reason for survival.

Emotions, feelings that move us, are of many varieties. Primitive emotions such as rage and fear were first developed during the evolution of the lower animals, when they had great survival value. Rage, for example, is a powerful reflex emotion, arising on the level of instinct. It is induced by the release of hormones which induce powerful chemical changes in the body, and we can feel them for hours after losing our temper. These hormones increase blood pressure and set free new chemical energy for nerves and muscles. A cat can fly into a rage even after its higher brain has been removed. In civilization rage has little long-range survival value, and it is slowly being brought under control. Automobile drivers who shout at one another at street intersections are giving vent to the elementary emotion of rage because they find themselves in new situations of conflict for which higher forms of control have not yet been built into most of us. Amusing situations develop when one finds the opposing driver at whom he bared his teeth like a wildcat, to be an acquaintance, or his boss.

Such actions of the id are, in more familiar situations, kept under control by the superego, if not by the reason and intelligence of the ego. However, though one can learn to keep himself from becoming boiling mad, getting butterflies in the stomach before making a speech or an appearance on the stage is not yet so amenable to control in most of us.

The affection of a dog for his master is a much higher type of emotion than rage. Still higher types have been developed only during the human phase of development of the brain, and many of these are extremely complex. Such emotions as love and loyalty are integrated aspects of the inner mind which should be distinguished from the simple emotions which result from direct chemical release. Yet all emotions are related to body chemistry, both as cause and effect; a good visible example is the flood of tears, made directly from blood, that comes with rapid emotional release. Science is now making progress in revealing the origins and structures of many of our emotions which, affected both by sensation and by thought, like them are the end-products of electrochemical reactions, and can be profoundly affected by the molecules called drugs and hormones.

Emotional urges are still sufficiently strong in most human beings to prevail at crucial times over the dictates of reason. Wisdom involves awareness of when they should prevail. Love is blind, and rightly.

We do not understand our emotions as well as we might, because we respond to many of them in a logarithmic rather than a linear manner, as is also the case with our sensory responses. Doubling our troubles at times when we are relatively free from worry may more than double our anxiety, whereas to a person already suffering greatly, the same troubles added to his load may appear trifling. The childless matron whose principal interests center around the bridge table and the beauty parlor is likely to be forced by circumstances to turn up the gain of her psychological amplifiers to the point where, to get any signals of enjoyment from life, she must suffer from much meaningless static. Such an individual is likely to feel that she suffers more than her pioneer prototype who had to labor fourteen hours a day spinning her own cloth and raising a large family. The pioneer woman was often happier, not because she led a simpler life, but because the mental, emotional, and spiritual signals she received from life were more meaningful.

We frequently hear science blamed for making our modern lives ever more complicated. Primitive life, in point of fact, had many complications, which primitive man was not any more fit to meet than we are fit to meet our complications today. The human spirit possesses an automatic volume control which enables it to meet adversity to the degree that is required of it.

Because of the special kind of evolution that women have undergone in their functions as mothers and internal guardians of the family, they are more expert in the use of emotions than men. They use them for communication, for control, and for reaching conclusions through what is often called intuition. In a social gathering containing women all sorts of things happen of which any men present are likely to be unaware. Women are more interested than men in ceremonies such as weddings or funerals, because these are funneling devices for concentrating streams of emotion so that they can be intensified, modified, or dissipated.

Man is formalizing his emotional abilities through art as he formalizes his mental abilities through science. One purpose of art is to express beauty, calling forth a basic human aesthetic emotional response. The structure of an art form, whether music, painting, or poetry, is based on design, symmetry, harmony, and various other kinds of order. Life consists of patterns in space and in time. We are stimulated emotionally by observing these patterns, and by reproducing them through various mechanisms. There are patterns in the rhythm of music, in the flow of a landscape, or in the cadences of poetry. Modern painters, poets, and composers who claim to be seeking to shake off the shackles of order are merely seeking it on a different level. There is no art in chaos.

Poets use symbolism and imagery, developing them with rhythm, symmetry, and harmony. In writing a poem, the poet may not mind if it is logically incorrect or even unintelligible to many reasonable persons, if it will produce the desired emotional reaction in some. No one need be bothered by the fact that Keats has Cortez instead of Balboa standing on a peak in Darien, nor need we worry if Kipling's old Moulmein pagoda is nowhere near the sea. Instead of painting a picture which tells more than a thousand words, the poet tries to make one word invoke a thousand pictures. The highest forms of poetry produce mental as well as emotional reactions, and if really great art, spiritual reactions as well.

In music we respond emotionally to rhythmic patterns in time, to the melodic successions of pitch, and to harmonies. The response to music has evolved greatly in the past few centuries, and can be cultivated rapidly. Primitive peoples respond mainly to rhythm. At a later stage they come to appreciate melody, and then harmony. At first men did not like to listen to two tones at once. Then, only a few centuries ago, they began to like the octave, the sounding of two simultaneous tones whose vibration rates were in the ratio of two to one. Vibration ratios of three to two seemed bizarre then, but later they came to be pleasing. Then four to three, five to four, and six to five came into favor. In modern music such ratios as nine to eight or even thirteen to eleven are found pleasurable by the elect, while the simpler ratios alone seem vapid. Thus our emotions evolve rapidly with experience.

Scientists usually make poor poets, for they are likely to

depend too much on reason, and their product to invoke un-
desired emotional responses. Sir Isaac Newton called poetry
"ingenious nonsense." But science is beautiful for the same
reasons as poetry—because it contains symmetry, pattern, and
harmony. The poet, painter, and musician have no monopoly
on the creation of beauty, for the ardor of the creative artist
fills the scientist also when he pursues a discovery, and longs
for the perception of previously unknown truths.

To a mathematician the orderliness of numbers can bring
feelings of great beauty. One mathematician called the alge-
bra of determinants "a beautiful garden open on every side
to expansion." What tremendous emotions must have surged
through Galileo when he saw for the first time through his
telescope four tiny moons circling about Jupiter! As he per-
ceived their positions changing on successive evenings, his
creative imagination saw demonstration of the lofty concept
that the planets revolve, and his mind jumped to the idea that
the earth revolves around the sun, and therefore need not be
considered the center of the universe. This sweep and play
of beauty extends throughout the whole of science.

One reason that artists, especially Bohemian writers, poets,
painters, and composers, lead such complex and often unhappy lives is that they tend to abandon themselves to strong
emotional reactions, which through unbalance increase the
rigors of their experience. An easy but unpleasant way to
obtain the true feeling of tragedy is to experience the natural
results of self-abandon, giving the id its head. Much modern
literature is little more than the recording of experiences to
which the writers have abandoned themselves, not always
taking care even to keep out of jail or the madhouse. The
true genius needs no such artificial aids, for his creative imagination substitutes adequately for reality, and he is thus the
better able to bring forward new integrations of human experience.

Man needs to understand things emotionally as well as through thought. Science has contributed much to art with radio, television, motion pictures, and other art forms which, though now in their elementary stages of development, will add much to the flexibility of emotional as well as intellectual expression. Science need not be a menace to the poet, for it can enhance rather than obscure the deeper and real values of life.

4

The type of personality to which society owes most of its progress is the genius. There are geniuses of physical co-ordination, such as champion golfers and baseball home-run kings, geniuses of the emotions, like Beethoven and Shelley, geniuses of the intellect, like Aristotle and Einstein, and of the spirit, like Buddha and Confucius. Some geniuses even excel in two or more of these aspects, as did Shakespeare. While they are likely not to lead balanced and happy lives, they often achieve great fulfillment of creation and attain a deeper joy thereby.

The influence on human progress of a true genius may extend over hundreds and thousands of years, and even over the whole of subsequent history. Aristotle, Galileo, Newton, and Einstein were giants of the intellect who altered the entire course of science. Like such men as Michelangelo, Leonardo da Vinci, and Shakespeare, they had strong imaginations, deep insight, and a vast ability to generalize. They could see through the surface aspect of things to the fundamental structures of life beneath, and were able to express these in ways other men find good.

Genius in a personality is likely to make itself known early in life, as with child prodigies of the violin and of mathematics. Newton and Einstein both did their most important work before the age of twenty-six. Geniuses are always persons with a consuming interest in their specialties, and are most clearly characterized by the addition of imagination to concentration. Thus genius is not merely a matter of intelligence—in fact, some of the outstanding geniuses have been rather unintelligent people. This is especially true in the case of geniuses who deal with emotional rather than intellectual activities.

Nature has developed at least three successful ways of solving problems. The first, that of organic evolution, is trial-and-error. Try every possibility, let the things that do not work perish, and in time you develop many devices that work very well. When the brain had reached a certain degree of elaboration it became possible to arrive at similar ends much more quickly, and by reason to rule out in anticipation many experiments doomed to failure. Then came a third method—the use of imagination, which enables man to save much of the effort of logic, and to jump by intuition to conclusions which he can then test.

True intuition is like a leap forward in the dark, across an empty space, which ends with one finding himself on solid ground again. Every scientific generalization is intuitive, for while the scientist may see a phenomenon just by looking, as at Newton's apple, he can use creative imagination and intuition to relate this apple to the moon, and so discover the Universal Law of Gravitation.

Creative imagination is one of the most important activities of the mind, and is that in which geniuses excel. It results from inspiration. It is made possible by our remarkable capacity to see in what we call the mind's eye images of things that our eyes have never seen. The unconscious mind puts patterns together in all sorts of arrangements. Inspiration appears to come when a very striking or important pattern emerges from the workings of the unconscious into the conscious. Most mental patterns in the unconscious are meaningless, or useless, and the images they would produce are faulty, but as they go boiling around a striking set occasionally gets together. These are then directed up into the conscious mind of a person who has a fertile imagination.

Poets frequently emphasize that they do not know what a poem is to be about until they have finished it. This has been taken by some to indicate that inspiration comes from outside the mind, but it appears rather to come from the unconscious mind. Much of the poem is put together there, and it is dredged out, either in pieces or as a whole, into the conscious where it can be dried off and polished up.

Usually the patterns that come to mind are not perfect when they reach the conscious, but produce a feeling that they can be made more so. This perfecting of the results of inspiration is the "nine-tenths perspiration" of genius. Beethoven's notebooks show that he often rewrote passages for his symphonies a dozen times, each revision showing recognizable improvement. But different people are inspired differently. Mozart apparently dredged his compositions up from his subconscious almost complete. He said that he saw a composition as a unit like a cathedral, rather than as successive tones. Thus he was able to perceive symmetries in structure, and with his whole composition in mind before he began conscious work, could put down the notes very quickly. This is often true also in literature. Coleridge is said to have written Kubla Khan at feverish speed after it came to him whole on waking from a nap. He was interrupted before he completed writing down the poem, and as he was never able to recapture the vision, his gem remains a fragment.

Sometimes an artist or a scientist does much conscious work before his unconscious begins the rearrangement of patterns. Many a scientist or inventor has had the experience of starting to work on a problem, and coming to an apparently dead end. Then, after putting it aside for days or months, he may suddenly come on the solution. The subconscious mind has been working actively on the problem, even during sleep. Often the solution will emerge while the thinker is in church, or at a concert, or just on waking, when the conscious mind is immersed in emotional activities, or the channels between the unconscious and the conscious minds are less active than usual.

Some people believe that genius is the result of suffering, and that one result of science may be to reduce the supply of geniuses as modern living makes men more comfortable. This is a dubious inversion. Those geniuses who suffer unduly usually do so because they are somewhat unbalanced in personality. The general belief that genius is akin to madness arises because genius is usually associated with an extreme sensitivity of some aspect of the human mind. By analogy, consider a photographic emulsion, which ordinarily is insensitive to some colors of light. If the emulsion is warmed up by exactly the right amount for the right time, its grains can be made so sensitive that it will record images to which an ordinary plate is insensitive. However, if the heating be carried too far, many grains of the emulsion spontaneously release their silver into black specks, and show images where no light has struck at all. So it may be with a mind too sensitively attuned to the sensations of the outer world, or to its own inner cogitations.

Sir Isaac Newton, who between twenty and twenty-five had one of the greatest minds in history, is said to have become a schizophrenic at the age of fifty. Beethoven drank excessively, was a very difficult person to get along with, and came close to madness. Edgar Allan Poe was addicted to drink, and was a melancholic. Tolstoi suffered from both melancholia and hysteria. However, the genius-akin-to-madness idea must not be pushed too far, for there is probably as much madness in proportion among people who are not geniuses as among those who are, and many great geniuses, such as Leonardo da Vinci and Shakespeare, were far from mad.

As time goes on, the world needs and will have more geniuses, not only because the number of human beings is increasing, but because we are learning how better to seek out genius, and give it greater opportunities for expression. Many potential geniuses never become active today because of lack of opportunity. The internal pressures of genius can be stimulated or retarded by external circumstances. Humanity needs balanced genius so much that we cannot afford to overlook any reasonable means for its production.

5

The phrase "You can't change human nature" springs from a short-range view. What is human nature? The shape of the human jaw and the size of the human brain pan have changed quite markedly in the last one hundred thousand years. So have man's responses to his environment. The relative importances of desire, reason, and conscience often shift quite suddenly, and through survival values remain shifted beneficially. The patterns governing a young man's operation of his mental switches can be changed quite markedly in a few months, by education.

Probably there has been little change up or down in man's average intelligence, as measured by reasoning ability and basic educability, during recorded history. A few thousand years is too short a time for mutation and selection to have produced much improvement in the basic intelligence level, although one can never tell when a mutation will suddenly produce a more complex and usable brain in some son of man, as has happened many times in the past, which will catch on and eventually spread throughout the whole race.

It turns out that the level of average intelligence in the various present races of mankind varies little. Some Australian aborigines have shown themselves as able as anyone to profit by education. One of the highest IQ's ever measured was that of a little colored girl who had no white blood. The lack in the suppressed races seems to be not brain capacity, but opportunity. In the United States even climate appears to have a much greater effect on intelligence than does race, although this effect is more likely to be one of body chemistry as it affects the measurement and use of intelligence than on true intelligence itself.

Education can be used to develop civilized responses very rapidly in almost any human being. Natives on the Pacific islands around Manus and New Guinea were visited by the anthropologist Margaret Mead in 1928, and again twenty-five years later. During her first visit they were entirely primitive, living in the equivalent of the Stone Age. In the intervening generation, in large part as a result of their contact with American soldiers during World War II, they learned many new social customs, became law-abiding, and appeared less greedy and quarrelsome. Almost any savage tribe can be civilized in this way.

Though our average ability to be educated improves but slowly over the centuries, our methods of education, poor as they still are, often improve very rapidly. Social forms of development are now becoming relatively much more important to the individual than those involving changes in the genes; the id comes under better control, the superego becomes more powerful, and desire, reason, and conscience become better integrated in certain groups of humans. Such advances are to a great degree under the control of man himself.

Classicists love to point out the great intelligences that arose during the days of Greece's grandeur, and the insinuation is widespread that modern man suffers greatly by comparison. There was, to be sure, a great flowering of achievement in classical antiquity, sparked by a few persons of intelligence quite as high as any we see today. But two thousand years is insufficient time to measure a change in level among such towering peaks, which we have now as we had then. Newton and Einstein lived as close together in time as Aristotle and Thales. The peaks that rose from the plane of thought when intellectual adventure was new are hard to measure, and it may well have been easier to reorient the ideas of men when there were fewer of either men or ideas. But the change in direction wrought by Newton and Einstein on the common run of thought was certainly not exceeded by any ancient Greek. They reared their structures on a massif left by many minds, but their influence on the reasoning and actions of mankind is likely in the end to make men think of a few only as their peers. Certainly there has, over the past ten thousand years, been an easily detectable increase in imagination, and certainly a great increase in insight, on the part of much of humanity.

To be convinced of this, one may need to use a longer yardstick, and go back even before the beginnings of the human brain. An ant cannot learn much as an individual. It is the ant colony as a whole that slowly learns, and an ant that tries something new is likely to be killed off unless his innovation is so successful, as a result of a useful mutation, that it becomes permanent. An earthworm, further along the path of progress, can be taught to turn left or right for food. Rats, still higher in awareness, are not able to reason much, but can solve problems, such as separating round objects from

triangular ones when these have to do with food or health.
Cats can be taught still more, and young dogs a great deal, so
we can see variations of intelligence appearing among individuals.

As indicated by the saying, "You can't teach an old dog
new tricks," dogs more than two years old lose learning ability rapidly. Chimpanzees can be educated up to the age of
about twelve years, beyond which they can't learn much
more. Such advanced types of apes can learn by insight as
well as trial-and-error. They can be taught to work for
money when they have learned that money will buy food.
In one notable case where a psychologist had provided three
ways for an ape to get bananas hung too high for him to
reach, the ape used none of these, but invented a fourth way
of which the psychologist had not thought.

Of all creatures, man has the greatest possibility of being
educated, and because of his complexity, needs education
most. Most humans can be educated in the ordinary sense
during their first forty years, and many can digest certain
types of learning up to eighty or more. The first third or so
of the lifetimes of most human beings in civilized lands is
now devoted to the development of their plastic physical,
emotional, mental, and spiritual bodies. Nowadays we spend
up to forty percent of our normal lives in being formally educated, and this fraction can be expected to increase.

Natural learning is a pleasant process, but our modern
educational system suppresses much of the joy that normally
comes with the rousing and satisfaction of curiosity. His
basic curiosity is one of man's great motivations toward education. Much of modern education has the effect of erasing
this by setting the same standards of achievement for every
child, in the name of democracy, regardless of his capabilities.
We should look further into the differences between moti-
vated and nonmotivated education. Both kinds are needed,

for each of us needs a certain fraction of discipline as well as of expression, but the two sorts of education need different approaches.

Much of the educative process in our schools today consists merely of instruction, which is the mere conveying to the student of new facts and ideas, and of training, which is the development of new skills. These are both important parts of education, but alone or together are not sufficient to produce an educated man.

Various authors have listed the qualities that a true education should develop in the mind. These include the ability to concentrate, which means learning to keep external or internal sensations from confusing the circuits among our mental switchboards; accuracy of observation, which involves learning to connect the nerve endings bringing in sensations into the proper mental associative circuits; retentiveness of memory, which requires exercising of the brain's storage mechanisms by repeated and new associations; logical reasoning, which is the exercising of switching patterns in formal groups in a way such that the currents which emerge will coincide with what the external world reveals; improvement in judgment, an even higher faculty that depends on predicting in advance, as a result of outer or inner experience, which circuits will best lead to a correct set of images; sensitivity of association, which involves developing the faculty of interconnecting vast swarms of switchboards without confusion, so that each on demand can be made sensitive to useful currents flowing in any others; and last and most important of all, creative imagination. This faculty is what influences human progress most greatly at present, and science, together with art and religion, is helping to advance its development.

One of the greatest defects of education in America today is its diffuseness. Teachers tend less and less to insist that their students learn to focus their attention on trains of thought which etch sharp patterns in the brain, instead of producing a chaotic opening and closing of mental switches at random, governed by the emotions of the moment. Disciplinary studies of the past, such as Latin and Greek, gave all sorts of little mental hooks on which associations could be hung. Science gives equally good associative hooks, and proper study of the humanities gives additional ones. But so superficial is much of our modern education becoming that many of the available mental hooks are not being provided for our citizens of tomorrow.

Great effects are being produced on man's spiritual nature, and on his basic balance as a human personality, by the changes induced by science in his security, his emotional reactions, his thought processes, his mental abilities, and his general awareness. These are helping to shift man's center of maximum response from the purely physical and emotional toward improved reason and understanding. This is the path to wisdom and spiritual advancement that must be trod if man is to become a balanced entity.

Chapter Eleven

Faith and the Scientist

$\mathbf{M}$any people today have the feeling that religion and science are in fundamental conflict. When the origins of this feeling are examined it is found that though to a considerable degree it arises from conflicting pressures of emotion and reason, these conflicts are neither basic nor irresolvable. The belief that science leads its devotees to be materialistic has many roots, not the least of which is an automatic confusion of "basic" with "base."

Examination of the personal beliefs of eminent scientists may not be enough to contradict this impression, but it is indicative. Sir Isaac Newton went to church regularly. He believed in a very real God who guided the operations of the Universe, but controlled the fall of each sparrow and the majestic cycles of the planets only through basic law. The Voice of God was to him a symbol for the laws under which the universe operates. Except in matters of cosmology he followed the dogmas of the Christian church, which he accepted as external symbols of great eternal truths. For guidance regarding nature he followed the observations of science, for he believed that religious teachings that concerned the stars and planets were mixtures of dogma with the science of an earlier era.

Galileo, while continuing during his house arrest for

heresy to deny under his breath that the sun goes around the earth, remained a good Catholic. Others long before him had maintained that the universe does not revolve around the earth as a center, but they were not so celebrated, and their heresy was not so dangerous. Galileo, despite short-term defeat, through his great intellectual vigor brought the new view of the whirling planets to ultimate acceptance by the world of men. Though waves of anti-intellectualism surged about him, his inner faith never left him, and he never left his church.

Einstein, though impatient of specific creeds and dogmas, was a deeply reverent man. He said, "To know the answer to the meaning of human life or the life of any creature means to be religious." He felt that no one could be really happy who did not follow the Law behind living. Other modern scientists who were as deeply religious, but in a more orthodox sense than Einstein, were Millikan, Jeans, and Eddington. Many others could be added to the list.

It would be futile to pretend that there has not been, and is not now, any conflict between scientific beliefs and religious creeds. Fully as much friction exists between them as among the creeds themselves. This friction occurs, however, almost entirely in the lower levels of specific dogma regarding the world of nature, and can be greatly reduced by more tolerance on all sides. Such tolerance appears to be growing.

Some scientists are quite as much to blame for intolerance as many mystics, although theirs is intolerance of a different sort. Many biologists are complete mechanists, treating man as nothing but an assemblage of organs which themselves are mere assemblages of molecules. Yet biologists know better than anyone else how foolish it is to think of any entity as merely the aggregate of its parts. There is much more to a violin than a collection of gut and wood and

lacquer and other particles, even though by analyzing molecules one is unable to find in it anything else. Far more
important than the matter the violin contains is the information that went into its design and assembly, and the emotional
reactions that it can bring to a listener. If real music comes,
who need worry about the habiliments of the player?

Some scientists are so overwhelmed by the discovery that
animal bodies are mechanisms that they tend to be literal in
their assessment of vitalism, and act like a child who has
just learned that there is no Santa Claus. Though the child's
earlier concept of Santa Claus was limited and incorrect, it
is better that he believe in a false Santa Claus for a time
than that he never grasp the spirit of Christmas at all. When
the wife of one eminent scientist asked him what she should
say in reply to their young son's question about whether
God really exists, he said, "Of course the answer is yes, because this will come much closer to what we consider the
truth than if you were to give the answer no." Yet this
man was what would be called an agnostic, or one without
knowledge, which does not conflict at all with the fact that
he was a deeply spiritual person.

Man can follow any of a great many paths in his quest
for truth. Of these the best defined at present are religion,
the arts, and science. Each has its own typical contributions
to make. Differences among them arise mainly from the
different aspect each reveals in its approach to the truth.
Within the last three centuries science has grown to be one
of the clearer paths to intellectual understanding, and of
this religion has great need. Scientists also have need, like
all men, to value the emotional and spiritual content of
living, with which they must be quite as much concerned
as are their nonscientific brothers.

The scientist, like the artist and the mystic, is dedicated
to the search for truth. The methods of science are designed

to distill realities from human experience mainly by way
of mental processes, and are calculated to separate the effects of emotion from those of reason. Yet every good
scientist must recognize the reality and importance of both
emotion and reason. He relies in his science on logic, but
also on inspiration, intuition, faith, love of beauty, and many
specific arts.

The technological progress that results from science, important to the world as it is, is far less important than the
intellectual and spiritual progress that science can help to
accelerate. Wisdom springs from balanced knowledge, and
the methods of science not only add to knowledge, but aid
in the attainment of balance. Science is helping humanity
to develop intellectual honesty, to learn to view truth objectively, and to reduce prejudices by weighing facts only
after examination.

Science confirms that we live in a universe which is
progressing. It conveys to men who will read its message
a sense of the endless possibilities of human progress. The
slow accumulation of human experience results in an uneven
but progressive increase in those spiritual qualities which
are of the utmost importance to man, and have great survival
value to the race—love, integrity, humility, sympathy, and
hope.

Spiritual values distill slowly from the interaction of sensation, emotion, and thought, which we have seen to depend
in turn on man's physical body, which again is formed
by his environment, which rests ultimately on the properties
of matter. It is not difficult for a scientist to see the hand
of God in the patterns which protons, neutrons, and electrons take in forming atoms, and those which the atoms take
to form molecules, molecules to form cells, cells to form
tissues, organs, and bodies, and bodies to form social aggregates. Science affects our understanding of all of these.

Even if one wishes to picture the eternal verities as spiritual values superposed on the character of man from a hidden universe within, science has much to offer in their interpretation.

2

No human society is known to have existed whose members have not developed religious beliefs, beginning with magic and leading to spiritual awareness. Even the lowliest Australian bushmen worship a spirit world. Today men belong to thousands of religious sects, the adherents of each of which usually consider their own the only true revealed religion. When the origins of belief are examined, it is apparent that the principal factor that determines a person's religious views is the religion of his parents, and the surroundings in which he spent the first few years of his life.

All religions are based to a rather large degree on the same spiritual truths, but differ in their emphasis on various aspects of those truths, and in the symbolism they use to make them comprehensible to the common man. Each sect reveals its portion of the spiritual waters in a container that gives to its revelation shapes and hues attractive and adapted to the mental, emotional, and spiritual status of its adherents. In each container some mud of superstition and magic is to be found mixed with the spiritual waters.

The world's sects of today have proliferated from eleven great religions, most of which are two thousand or more years old. Each was started by a great leader who had an unusual vision of basic spiritual truth. Each of the eleven has its sacred writings. Each when it began was remarkably similar to what the others were at their beginnings, but all have differentiated progressively as they congealed about the social customs of their adherents. Thus time has brought to all religious faiths an accumulation of dogma much of which was not there at the beginning.

Christianity is the most widely followed religion, having more than seven hundred million adherents divided into hundreds of sects. More than three hundred million Moslems follow the teachings of Mahomet, though they recognize Jesus also as a great spiritual teacher. Third religion in size is probably Buddhism, which like Hinduism, from which it originated some twenty-five hundred years ago as a sort of protestant reformation, has more than a quarter of a billion adherents. Confucianism, fifth in size, has nearly this number. These five most widely followed religions are much larger than the smaller six, which begin in size with Judaism, with some twelve million followers, and go down to Zoroastrianism, which has a mere one hundred thousand living adherents.

The relative amounts of ritual used and of mysticism followed vary greatly among the great religions, and within them. Many Tibetan Buddhist sects, for example, have degraded almost entirely into magic and witchcraft, with the wind-driven prayer-wheel representing the ultimate in mechanized supplication. Judaism concerns itself mostly with man's behavior, and is based primarily on ethics, strongly colored with Jewish tradition. Buddhism and Hinduism pay great attention to cosmology and man's relation to the universe. The Christian religions are noted for their emphasis on personal salvation, although in Jesus' day the present probably loomed much larger relative to the future than it does in Christianity today.

When one examines the great religions of the world in as dispassionate but sympathetic a scientific spirit as possible, recognizing that man is innately a religious creature with deep spiritual needs, one is struck by the fundamental similarity of their basic tenets, and by the superficiality of their differences. Many contradictory dogmas stem from such simple and materialistic causes as food customs, which in turn arose originally as matters of health in special climates. Moslems, Hindus, and Jews must not eat pork; Hindus must not kill cattle; various sects must not eat meat on Friday; Jewish food must be prepared by kosher, or clean, methods. Though many of the sanitary necessities which led to these customs no longer exist, the dogmas and rites which have resulted have the virtue of helping the adherent frequently reaffirm his connection with a long-standing line of social tradition. This gives him support, furnishes spiritual nourishment in a form which he can assimilate most readily, and stabilizes him against the buffetings of an all too uncertain world.

Nearly all the great world religions use what we Christians call the Golden Rule as a basic guide for conduct. Hindus have read for more than three thousand years, "Do not unto others that which if done to thee would cause thee pain." Buddhists hear, "Administer to your friends and familiars by treating them as you treat yourself." Confucianism has a Silver Rule, which says, "What you do not want done to yourself, do not do unto others." In Taoism the Teacher says, "To those who are good to me I am good, and to those who are not good to me I am also good." In Zoroastrianism, more than six hundred years older than Christianity, the statement is, "Whatever thou dost not approve for thyself, do not approve for anyone else." To the Jew comes the command, "And what thou thyself hatest, do to no man."

Four of the great religions lay special emphasis on monotheism, as a reaction against the degeneration of many polytheistic sects. For three thousand years the prayer of Judaism has been, "Hear, O Israel, the Lord our God, the

Lord is One." How similar this is to the first part of the prayer of the Moslem, "There is but one God, and Mahomet is His prophet." Both of these prayers can be taken as affirmations of the unity of all life, a belief which the scientist is confirming ever more completely. Given time, even monotheistic religions are likely to proliferate subdeities in the form of saints and relatives of God. Men need protective relatives as well as a Father. Thus the vast assemblages of lesser deities in such polytheistic cults as those of Hinduism are not unique.

As time elapses after the passing from earth of the founder of a great religious movement, his spiritual disciples come to depend more and more on the letter of his word, and this tends to become of equal importance to, or even greater importance than, the spirit of his teaching. Greater amounts of ritual and symbolism are developed to enhance the faith of the wavering. Though symbols appear to be religious necessities of any social structure, when they no longer enhance the inner vision but instead becloud it, their value becomes negative.

All great religions use miracles to bolster faith. Who was it who fed a large crowd of people with a small amount of food, healed the sick by touching or looking at them, and was able to walk on water? These miracles were ascribed to Buddha hundreds of years before Jesus was born, but Buddha was not the first. Priests have needed such devices to attract the attention of squabbling men to the Teachers who did many much more miraculous things for the human spirit.

A principal area of conflict between science and religious dogma can be in the literal interpretation of miracles. It is not that scientists cannot conscientiously believe in miracles if they want to, for science involves many acts of faith, and nothing is more miraculous than the detailed operations of nature. But a scientist is likely to resent any arbitrary suspension of a natural law. Although there is much in the universe which he cannot explain, it is important to him that the universe be as orderly as it looks when he experiments with it, and subject to law, not whim. Especially does he consider suspicious reports of miracles that occur under circumstances in which people strongly desiring a particular result have an interest, no matter how unselfish in origin, in influencing the beliefs of others, and show unwillingness to check their facts. Thus the scientist, whose inner light is as likely to take on an arbitrary coloration as that of anyone else, may come to have an undeserved reputation for lack of faith, when his faith is merely of a different sort.

Most dogmas represent useful holding operations designed to help suffering humanity visualize the eternal truths whose contemplation can give solace to the human spirit. A dogma is the emotional equivalent of a shelter, erected to protect a certain area of thought space in which are placed precious and needed utensils, and to hold away the great dark void of the unknown that presses about us all. Hence dogmas have a very important place in the erection and perpetuation of a religion that is to minister to the spiritual needs of the common man.

But dogmas retained too long restrain growth, or cause pain when growth occurs. The shell of a crustacean, useful to protect its soft body, becomes restrictive as it grows. This plastic armor must be split if expansion is to be accommodated. Science provides useful mechanisms for splitting outmoded dogmas. All of us need to shed our spiritual shells at times and grow larger ones, but we are likely when we do this to feel considerable tenderness until the new shell hardens.

Constant vigilance is needed on the part of priest and

preacher to keep the external expression of the inner principles of religion in pace with man's development. Science
helps in this by constantly feeding new information about
man and nature into religion, and producing growth which
prevents dogmas from remaining crystallized too long. Un-
derstandably some religious leaders resist such change, for
they are mortal custodians of eternal verities, and can be
expected to resent the cracking of the literalness that stiffens
the embodiment of a spiritual truth.

We may ask the scientist who resents the worshiping of
what seem to him false images of real truths, "What choice
has man, with his limited comprehension as he toils upward
on his path, but to get his light from the lamps he sees
about him? And who can blame him if during the earlier
parts of his climb he confuses the lamp with the light?"

3

All religions concern themselves with good and evil, and
teach ethics and morals. The essence of morality is the
balancing of immediate desires against long-term results. The
forces acting on a troubled spirit are usually active and
strong, whereas the long-term effects are likely to be tenuous
and extremely difficult to fix in mind. Nothing is more directly persuasive and immediate than body chemistry, yet
it is a poor guide to long-range human welfare. The chronic
alcoholic who wants another drink needs some stronger
force to dissuade him than the mere knowledge that he
and his family will suffer if he succumbs. Therefore, arbitrary laws are set up which present the problem as a simple
set of alternatives, with rewards and punishments bringing
reality to the symbolism.

The moral codes and principles of ethics of a social group

represent a distillation from long experience. To increase the tangibility of the long-term benefits of morality, teachers and prophets have learned to use various symbolic devices for making them more concrete and definite. One important aspect of every religion is its method of solving many basic psychological problems empirically, before their reasons for existing are fully understood. Now priest and psychologist are learning to walk side by side.

The human personality needs an uplifting force, a "sky hook" to draw man up from the downward pull of his lower desires. These are only base when misapplied. Man needs a vision of perfection, even though he often can evoke this only in terms of things long past, for the scaffolding that his faith erects is flimsy at best. The exact form his vision takes is relatively unimportant, so long as the end result gives him the needed ability to climb his shaky ladder toward the stars.

Most religions consist of two separable layers, one containing the revealed symbolism, and the other the arcane spiritual truths behind. The fact that the symbolic portions are creations of our own psychological needs does not make them any less real, good, or desirable, except when they are difficult to slough off after they have served their purpose. A twenty-year-old who still believes too literally in Santa Claus has difficulties.

Young people often rebel against moral codes because they feel that they are arbitrary, or a set of rules that were made so long ago that they are now old-fashioned and out-of-date. As man and his environment slowly change the rules too must change, but codes that represent the wisdom of society over the ages change very slowly indeed, like the shift of the polestar. We violate them at the peril of our own later suffering. This is likely to be the more grievous if the punishment is delivered automatically by nature than if as a result of infraction of one of man's protective rules.

Rebellion against society's standards of conduct can be reduced greatly among intelligent people when the rules can be properly explained and shown to be not arbitrary. Rebellion in excess usually indicates that the word of the teachings has become more important than its spirit, and a new set of directly controlling symbols is needed.

Many religions have a doctrine of Original Sin, considering all men as having been born evil, and only achieving salvation through special effort. This was probably originally symbolic of man's ignorance, from which he must grow through knowledge to wisdom. Man inevitably takes many wrong steps, and can be viewed as steeped in sin, first innocently, and later, as a result of mixed or improper motives. Perhaps most closely related to a scientific view is the basic tenet in Hinduism and Buddhism known as the law of karma, according to which all acts produce their results automatically, as effects follow causes. Punishment and reward are indistinguishable except in terms of the feelings of the individual, and are merely the automatic feedback reactions from a universe in which all parts are interrelated.

Humanity has made great progress in ethical development in the six thousand years of recorded history. While progress is intermittent, and some doubt that there has been any, a quantitative summing up should reveal to all but the most cynical that human progress has been great. Most of the Greeks and Romans of antiquity of whom classicists make so much were cruel and hard. Civilized people are coming to think it not right to kill a man merely because he steals food for his starving family. A merchant's word can be trusted more and more widely over the earth in the marts of trade. Most of the people alive today will still lie and steal and cheat if they think they can do this without being detected, but there are increasing numbers who will refrain from doing so even when there is no danger of detection. The conscience is coming to be an ever stronger inner light. We should not let the present concentration of ideological differences, which always cause much dross to float to the surface of the spiritual melting pot, to blind us to the basic realities of man's progress.

Virtue does have long-term survival value, even though the good appear at times to die young. Much of man's uncertainty as to cause and effect arises from the fact that the results of nature's operations must be taken statistically rather than as individual cases. This is true even in the physical laws of the universe, where cause and effect seem to break down in specific occurrences, but do not if groups of happenings are averaged.

It is not so much fatuous to say that we live in the best of all possible worlds as it is meaningless. But our world does appear to be getting better all the time. Despite apparent increases in conflict and uncertainty, order can be seen to be spreading. Order does not spread by itself, and many of us get great comfort from feeling this spreading of order in the universe to be one of the manifestations of a force we can call God.

4

A public opinion poll taken recently is said to have indicated that 96 percent of all the citizens of the United States now believe in God. This could probably be stated more correctly in the inverse form: not more than 4 percent of United States citizens are so repelled by religious dogmas as to be willing to state that they do not believe in God. However, the kind of God they believe in varies greatly, as indicated by the reasons they gave for their belief. Most gave the visible order and majesty of the world around us. This reason is certainly acceptable to most scientists, who perceive additional inner layers of this order and majesty, and are willing to call the unifying force behind the universe God, provided too anthropomorphic a definition of the Creator does not then result.

Man has great natural reverence in his makeup, as well as mystical feeling, and he has much need for help and guidance in a complex world. For all of these religion has first responsibility, but science also can contribute and does. Conflicts between the two almost disappear if the origins of religious dogmas concerning the early days of man are understood, if tribal traditions and social customs are separated from the body of spiritual truth in scriptural writings, and if the natural tendency of people to believe what they want to believe is understood.

An empty skate-egg case lying on the beach, a little black rectangular pillow-shaped object, can arouse deep religious feelings, for it is provided with a coiled tentacle at each corner. This is to attach the case to a frond of seaweed, so that it will be swished through the water and aerated without being washed away. At once one tends to see a beneficent Creator arranging specifically for the protection of the eggs of young skates yet unborn. However, when one studies the picture of evolution and sees how the skate eggs and their cases arrived at this form only after many millions of years of development, as nature tried first one experiment and then a million others, the view is likely to change. One sees then rather a Creator that provided impulse and impetus, order and a guiding law, and then left the development of the skate to the unfolding of this law. Yet what do we mean here by "leaving," for the order and impetus are everywhere, and the scientist, like the mystic, can, if he will, see the hand and face of God in every act and creature. Most religious people find it entirely acceptable nowadays to believe that God set up a system in which organic evolution was then able to take place.

Scientists have a special responsibility not to destroy religious reverence with scientific criticism unless the two are in head-on collision, which is seldom the case. There is nothing to be gained from forcibly shaking the faith of another without substituting a larger faith that can be embraced with equal fervor and from which equal support can be derived. Scientists who slash vindictively at men's beliefs deserve censure when they cannot furnish an acceptable substitute. Many present-day dogmas are likely to be scabs covering old wounds, and should not be picked at until the flesh beneath is firm.

It is difficult for humans to conceive of a creative act without something corresponding to a personality to carry it out. Thus a God is a necessity for most men. Because we are humans we picture God as a more perfect edition of ourselves.

Fundamental to all great religions is their catering to man's desire for immortality. One of the major preoccupations of men is to get a picture of life after the body is dissolved. We do not like the idea of losing self-uniqueness. Our desire for continuity of consciousness has arisen from the desirability of preservation of the individual, important for many of nature's purposes as she evolves by tying up her elements in packets. Though some religions stress immortality more than others, without exception they teach that there can be a continuity of consciousness beyond death.

Belief in immortality is not contrary to any teaching of science, for science has no evidence regarding it. It is a matter of individual belief and acceptance of authority—that is, of faith. Many scientists are prepared to take immortality on faith; others feel that while a life after death is to be desired the only evidence that there is such is indirect. Still others say that they have seen no evidence yet one way or another, but they know how prone humans are to believe anything which appeals to them strongly, and that the desire for immortality has strong emotional appeal. Still others feel that from our observations of life, the simplest explanation is to say that human consciousness does not continue after death, for in the absence of evidence to the contrary one should assume the simplest hypothesis until it is proved incorrect. But science has no direct evidence that men's souls are not immortal. Especially does it not have enough to justify interference with the faith in immortality of any believing person. Instead it has great comfort to offer those who wish verification of the innate feeling they have regarding the order of the world, and of the vast reaches of the cosmos.

5

The difficulties men have in visualizing God are in some ways similar to those scientists have in visualizing the atom. Both are important to humans, but most directly so on levels of perception far removed from that on which humanity is based. We can visualize them only in terms of their effects on levels we can contact. Scientists have had to change their ideas of atoms many times, picturing them always in terms of what atoms do to humans and their world. We talk glibly about the appearance of an atom, and discuss what it might look like if it were big enough to see, forgetting for the moment that the phrase is meaningless. An atom, being essentially unseeable, can have no appearance. The phrase "to see" has real meaning only in terms of waves of light af-

fecting eyes, and waves of light are much too long to give
an image of any atom. Nevertheless, scientists are getting
ever clearer ideas of what an atom is and does, and insofar
as they are able more successfully to predict the behavior of
atoms under various circumstances, we say that their ideas
are correct. So is it with man's concept of God.

The sum total of human experience points, like the compass needle toward the magnetic pole, fairly definitely in a
certain direction. Men need a polestar, and so long as their
star leads them in approximately the correct direction, what
matter if they all do not follow the same one? The star
Polaris has served to guide mariners for more than ten centuries, and we think of it as indicating true north, but actually
it does this only roughly. Furthermore, its position slowly
shifts over the ages. Centuries ago Polaris was many degrees away from the pole, and the earliest sailors used an
entirely different star to indicate north.

Similarly, the mariner's compass indicates the magnetic
rather than the true north. The magnetic North Pole is
found to be many hundreds of miles away from the true
North Pole when you get there. When a plane flies over
the apparent position of the magnetic pole, no pole can be
found. Yet the magnetic compass does operate well over
most of the earth, and where would a navigator be without
one? Thus the preacher and the teacher should not occupy
themselves too much with forms of higher criticism for the
beginner at religious knowledge, but should rather try to
orient him in a general way, and trust that new stars and
compasses will be available to guide him as he becomes able
to use them.

There is great need in the world today for a new integration of religious belief, which will fill all the innate
longings of man for spiritual solace, without doing too much
violence to his intelligence. It should give him the comfort

and consolation he needs in adversity, but at the same time be based on newer symbols and more flexible dogmas. Science can help in this. Buddha anticipated a basic tenet of science when he wrote, "Believe nothing merely because you have been told it, or it has been traditional, or because you yourselves have imagined it. Believe whatsoever you find to be conducive to the good, to benefit the welfare of all things."

Over the ages men's reactions to stimuli slowly change, and gradually these changes affect their thought processes, their emotions, and their spiritual vigor. Consider the ability to put one's self in another's place, called empathy, a technical word for application of the Golden Rule. A century ago even in America one of the fundamental freedoms was the right to starve to death. A beggar could lie dying in the gutter and people would walk by him unconcerned. Today, at least in lands where the standard of living has been raised by science to the point where the scramble to keep alive does not take up most of human effort, empathy has developed to the point where no one is refused food or hospitalization. Two thousand years is but a flick of time in which to look for changes in men's intellect, but it is not too short a time to look for changes in his spirit.

Science is affecting human thought in many ways. Not the least of these is that it helps to shift man's center of response from the physical and emotional toward reason and understanding. The mechanistic parts of our civilization were not selected by scientists as alternatives to living in a world in which spiritual values would otherwise come uppermost. Nor should scientists be accused of materialism when they seem preoccupied with material things, for the living universe needs the granite of the hills on which to rest, and the characteristics of the grosser fundament affect the citadel above. The things spiritual with which we should be most concerned have in this world physical, emotional, and mental embodiments. Our progenitors were physical creatures first, and later grew to have emotional, then mental, and ultimately spiritual aspects and attitudes. It is not possible to develop the refined essences of the spirit, at least in this world we know, without having the grosser essences to form bases for development.

Great effects are produced on man's spiritual nature, and on his basic balance as a human being, by the changes induced through science in man's security, his emotional reactions, his thought processes, his abilities, and his general awareness of the world about him. In America today all sorts of good causes find very broad response, and there is much warmheartedness in the pioneer countries where progress in the social order is dynamic.

The basic tenets of all great religions, the distilled spiritual wisdom of humanity, coincide closely with what science reveals in nature. The universe is based on order, not on chaos and chance. Man can improve his environment, his own nature, and his opportunities. Through co-operative effort new entities can be formed from lesser components, which give greater purpose and achievement to existence. There is direction to living that gives stability in the midst of change. These things the ancient sages knew; science helps make them more apparent to us all.

Chapter Twelve

What Man May Yet Become

The great and constant need of every human being is a feeling of certitude. Like the calcium that stiffens the cells of bone and body, both faith and knowledge are needed to give tone to the cells of our spiritual makeup. When the forces of change are as active as they are today, we have special need for the support that comes from awareness of the basic trends that underlie the superficiality of events. The systematic understanding of nature's laws that science makes possible can throw much light on the age-old questions of why we are here and where we are going, insofar as these questions can be answered in human terms.

Young people especially are likely to be uncertain in these days of shifting social values. They are not helped by the counsels of those philosophers who, overly preoccupied with previous eras when living was more simple, see man now fighting a losing battle against gathering forces of complexity and uncertainty. To such observers man's best hope is merely to hold his own if he cannot regain his status of the Golden Age (golden from a distance, because of the absorption of blue and indigo hues by a millennium or two). The traditional humanistic studies, such as history and the classical arts, acquaint us with man's past, and help us in many ways better to understand ourselves, but the short

record of human history covers less than one percent of the
more than a million years that men have walked the earth.
Science, reading the record that stretches back to the beginnings of the world, can add much to put man in proper
perspective in his view of nature.

We need to concern ourselves more than we do with
man's future. There is a fashion today of assuming glibly
that he may have no future; that with his new atomic powers,
and his eternal selfishness, he is likely to wipe his kind completely from the earth. Such a view ignores the many basic
stabilizing forces that nature has developed in her creatures
over the slow course of evolution, and to date man is her
most effective creation. Men respond to new challenges, and
are happiest when there are new challenges to which to
respond.

Whether nuclear power will bring man more happiness
or less depends on how he uses it. I can hear the chairman
of a panel set up in the early Pleistocene era asking, "Will
this new thing called fire bring us happiness or tragedy? It
has already burned up our best hunting woods." Fire has
indeed brought humanity both happiness and tragedy.
Would we then be better off not knowing about it? The
vaster and more profound combustions involving the atomic
nucleus will bring us both greater happiness and greater
tragedy. We shall end up by learning how to avoid the
tragedy; the only question is as to how much suffering will
be needed to teach us the new lessons set before us.

In this connection it is interesting to note the two major
changes in American public opinion regarding the atomic
bomb that have occurred between 1945 and 1955. At first
we were rather smug about it; we had developed a powerful
new bomb that had been proved capable of stopping a great
war and saving millions of lives. Then, when it became
evident that the Russians also had the bomb, which American

laymen at first thought possible only as a result of Russian subversion of a few scientists, it suddenly became a very evil thing, and a weapon which might result in the disappearance of civilization. Later still, when our development of defensive measures against bombing and our maintenance of superior striking power obviously began to force the Russians to place less reliance on force and to have recourse again to devious means, it became evident that by its very terror the bomb might bring men into less violent methods of working out their differences. Thus a new level of world co-operation begins to appear possible, as the normal checks and balances of behavior begin to spread more widely over world politics.

Efforts toward a unified world government are at present in the stage of political evolution of one of the less stable Central American republics. Men get better governments only when they develop civic virtues on the proper scale, and become willing to pay their taxes honestly and make the sacrifices necessary for the common good. A few decades of experience will bring great progress, of which we can already see evidences in the effect of the actions of the United Nations on world opinion.

One hears grave warnings that this may be the final hour for choosing whether science is to be misappropriated for human folly and destruction, or embraced for salvation and a good way of life. If there were such a single hour this might well be it, but life has been, and will continue to be, a perpetual succession of such hours. Science is merely a special way of accumulating knowledge, and most of our progress since man first attained the ability to reason has resulted from the making of just such choices as to how each new bit of knowledge was to be applied.

To behave effectively in his physical universe, man needs to become increasingly a prophet. He needs to improve wherever possible his ability to predict the outcome of a given course of action. Much of the difficulty that the classically minded philosopher finds in predicting the future of man arises from the shortness of the span of events which he must extrapolate. In the language of modern communication engineering, the signal-to-noise ratio of history is still extremely low. We need all the information we can get about the relation of man to the universe, and can fill in the deficiencies of the classicist's thumb-breadth of human history with the long ruler of nature's record.

The social scientist studying man's behavior is now somewhat in the position of a physicist trying to discover the law that governs the change in pressure of a gas as its temperature is varied, when he can observe only a few million molecules, has watched them for only a few seconds, and finds that their indiscriminate collisions almost completely obscure the trends that indicate their over-all behavior. Such an observer would be likely to say, "Molecules are unpredictable." In point of fact molecules, while unpredictable as individuals, are very predictable in the mass. So too are men, as we shall learn when we are more acutely aware of the laws that govern their behavior.

Most scientific philosophers have in the past had an inborn feeling that anyone who really knew enough of the present state of a world or a universe, and what had happened to it in the past, could predict what would happen to it in the future. Recently they have been greatly shaken by the discovery of a law of nature, now usually called Heisenberg's Uncertainty Relation, which indicates that no one can predict exactly how an electron or other tiny particle will move if he knows exactly where it is, or conversely, can find where such a particle is if he can predict how it will move. This has been taken by some as meaning that there is no possibility of predicting the future, but such is not the case.

Heisenberg's law indicates that we cannot predict individual actions on the sub-atomic level as exactly as we thought, and that the very act of making an observation affects any particle we may observe. Thus we appear to possess no one-way windows through which to scan the universe, like those through which teachers can watch children at play without being themselves observed. It well may be that such dissociation will always be impossible. However, Heisenberg's relation may later be found to arise from our present limited understanding of quantum phenomena, and in any case has to do only with individual actions on a very minute scale. In terms of the statistics governing the behavior of millions of particles there is much that can be predicted from the vantage point of men.

Science is doing more than any other human activity to improve man's gifts of correct prophecy. Scientists do their best prophesying when they get away from individual events, and work on broad generalizations. Einstein, a great genius at generalizing physical principles, was guided in his investigations by deep feelings regarding the unity, symmetry, and uniformity of behavior of nature. He was confident that the universe is governed by fundamentally simple laws. He looked for mathematical equations which would fit these convictions and the observed facts, and by following a combination of scientific, aesthetic, and philosophical principles, developed in his Relativity a theory relevant to the behavior of energy from the innermost parts of the atom to the outermost observable reaches of the cosmos.

Within the framework of what we know, it is possible to predict in general where mankind seems likely to be headed, even though these predictions depend not so much on what scientists do with matter and energy as on what men do to each other. Before embarking on any attempt to read the future, however, we need to consider more fully the two important questions, What is truth? and What is good? With our answers to these questions may come an inkling of one answer to that age-old question, Why are we here? All of these are involved in our query when we ask what man may be.

2

How can one tell what things are true? What is the meaning of reality? Answering such questions has always been doubly difficult for philosophers because of the confusion between objective and subjective reality. From one point of view, the final judge of truth for each of us must be the "I" within himself. Yet we feel a desire to be able to picture the universe and all within it on an absolute basis, as it might exist apart from any observer, for we find it hard to visualize as many real universes as there are humans who are aware of them. Furthermore, in recent years scientists have discovered, largely through such verified theories as Einstein's Relativity, that our feeling that there is such a thing as absolute reality is incorrect, and that truth is always relative. There are many overlapping regions in which subjective and objective are inseparable.

The discoveries of science show that we all live in worlds of illusion, as Eastern mystics long have held. But once we understand what an illusion is, we find that this is a perfectly reasonable sort of world to live in. We must learn to live with illusions while recognizing them for what they are, for through them lie our only approaches to reality.

Most of our illusions come from only partial understanding. As a simple but useful illusion of this sort, consider the common belief that camels carry in an extra stomach quantities of water which they use to slake their thirst on long desert journeys. The truth behind this misapprehension is even more interesting than the statement itself. Camels have no extra stomach for water, I am told, but store fat in their humps. Water is then produced from this when the fat is burned for its energy. Even more important to the camel are the mechanisms it has developed to enable it to get along on relatively small amounts of water. It sweats very little. It keeps its mouth closed to conserve moisture, and does not pant like a dog. It can tolerate much greater increases in body temperature than most other animals and so gets along without much evaporative cooling. It is better able than they to stand drying out, and remains healthy even when its blood becomes very viscous. By force of circumstances it has achieved the ability to accept semi-desiccation as a natural state. Thus, though the common concept of water-storage by camels is illusory, the illusion is useful in promoting, in those of us who have reached only a certain stage of awareness, an appreciation of the fact that the desert has made the camel a peculiar beast.

Among the famous concepts mentioned earlier in this book as exposed illusions is the luminiferous Aether. To get rid of this, Einstein had to disillusion all the scientists of the world. He did this by successfully contradicting what seemed and still seems to be the most obvious common sense. A bullet shot from a moving gun has a different velocity from one shot from a gun at rest, for to the motion of the bullet that of the gun must be added. This concept can logically be expected to apply to light waves observed by a scientist on a rapidly moving planet, but when this was done it led to gravely incorrect conclusions. Einstein's genius lay in having the ability and the willingness to see what had to be assumed to make the behavior of light come out as it is observed to be. By being so apparently foolish as to assume that light moves at a constant velocity relative to all observers, he picked up the vanished scent of truth and led the whole baying field of scientists, their tattered Aether in shreds, off in a new direction.

Is light a hail of photons, a streaming set of packets of energy, or is it ripples of some sort in space? Both pictures are found to be necessary to explain all the things that light is observed to do, yet in certain circumstances each picture conveys a false impression if taken too literally. Light waves have even been said to exist only as waves of knowledge. This is an extreme position that helps to jolt our minds free of preconceptions, but again it must not be taken too seriously, for indeed everything we are aware of consists, for us, of nothing but waves of knowledge. Though all our observations are illusions, unreal and to some extent misleading, those that enable us to predict future happenings correctly time after time come as close for us to reality as anything well can come. When the argument is pressed beyond this point we begin to wander around in philosophical circles.

We approach closest to reality in human terms when we set up a picture that enables us to predict correctly the outcome of some experiment or course of action. We do this by choosing those illusions, from among a great number, which enable us to make verifiable predictions on as many separate but connected levels of existence as possible. There is no reason to suppose that we get any closer to reality when scientists take us down into the realms of the atom and molecule than we are when observing phenomena in the external world. The gain in studying atoms is the new set of illusions which enables us to examine truth from new angles. Reality may well exist on every level of manifestation, but it must be interpreted on each in terms of our illusions so as not to involve contradictions with the illusions we reach from other views.

Consider the circular set of ripples that appears on the

surface of a quiet pond when a fish jumps. Depending on how our attention is caught, we see a succession of rings that move outward, or a ring system that stands nearly still as one ripple is replaced by another. Both pictures are illusions, for no water moves outward; water particles merely rise and fall as the ripples pass across them. The problem of reality can be compounded here still further by pointing out that the water is really nothing but an assemblage of molecules bouncing rapidly against one another, which take on minute additional drifts from each ripple. Or we can ignore the molecules, and the atomic particles of which they are composed, and say that the true reality of the rippling pond exists in a force field in space. All of these statements are true, but each is illusory in its own way. We approach closer to an understanding of the reality of the ripples when we see them in terms of all of these illusions together, each useful on its own level. Our physical universe, far more complex than ripples on a pond, needs to be looked at from as many angles as possible, and this is what science is designed to help us do.

We know now that matter is not a solid continuum, as it was supposed to be before atoms were discovered, and as it still appears to our unaided senses. Yet from the human standpoint the solidity of matter is a very useful illusion. When chopping solid wood with a very solid ax, it would be inconvenient to have to take into account the individual electrons and nucleons of which wood and ax are composed. Yet if we come to take apart the matter of which the ax is composed so that we can cause its atoms to emit light, we are greatly interested in the electrons which they contain. One illusion is useful in one connection, the other in another, but we are unhappy if they seem mutually contradictory, and feel we have an "explanation" only when they can be brought into agreement. Thus reality comes from the non-contradictory combination of illusions. We achieve greater awareness as we comprehend as many levels as possible, and attack our problems on the most effective levels for each.

The pictures painted by science are thus seen to be symbolic, just as are those of religion. When physicists make pictures of atoms they are not attempting to show how atoms really look, for, as we have seen, this would have no meaning. Rather they are trying to indicate what relationships exist between atoms and the rest of the universe, as interpreted on the human level of consciousness. To ask what a proton or an electron *really* is has no meaning either; we must ask rather how these particles behave in relation to humans, so that we can predict how they will affect us in any given situation. "Explaining" something consists in relating it to more familiar phenomena in such a way as to give a more unified picture of the universe.

Some of our illusions become illusory to an extra degree because we like to think of ourselves as in a static world rather than in one that is dynamic and changing. Everywhere about us is ceaseless motion, but of necessity we observe life in terms of snapshots, and until we can view each event from all angles, we fall into error as we attempt to assemble our impressions into a moving picture. Science shows us how to bring the needed all-inclusive view into better focus.

It is sometimes said that when we get away from the bustle of the city into the green fields we are getting closer to reality. However, in such a case we are merely getting closer to familiarity, for returning to nature restores us somewhat to the simplicity of our social past, and invigorates us with atavistic feelings, to say nothing of fresh air, exercise, and relaxation. But we enjoy the woods and fields the more because we know that we can later return to the complexities of modern living, which, though we may deride them, bring increased opportunities for self-expression.

3

How can one tell what things are good? The study of science has led many to the conclusion, long since reached by many philosophers and mystics, that there is no such thing as absolute good or absolute evil. Good and evil are among our most important symbols and illusions, and we need to understand them as measuring desirable and undesirable actions. We call that good which brings the maximum of integrated happiness, but must then define happiness correctly. Evil is that which brings physical or mental or emotional or spiritual pain. Good and evil can be viewed as lag and lead feedback forces which in the servomechanisms of living affect the behavior of the individual.

Physical pain is a form of evil which originates on the level of the body and is registered in the brain. Yet pain is both necessary and good. It is a very elementary sense mechanism, developed in early stages of animal evolution to give awareness of danger or harm. Like the other senses, it operates through electro-chemical pulses that travel along special nerve circuits from receptors in and on the body. Objectively pain is not at all disagreeable, any more than sweetness is of itself agreeable, but through long experience nature has taught animals to dislike pain, that is, to want less of it, for this has had great survival value.

Pain requires consciousness for its apprehension. Thus a toothache disappears when its possessor goes to sleep, although the signaling pulses still are there and the throbbing continues. Pain can be eliminated by stopping the excitation of the sensory pickups that send out pain signals, by blocking the nerve circuits from them to the brain, or by eliminating consciousness through sleep or anesthesia.

Because of the subjective character of pain the statement has been made that it is merely an illusion. This emphasizes the importance of illusions, and the correct answer was given by the celebrated "faith-healer of Deal, who said, 'Although pain is not real, when I sit on a pin, and it punctures my skin, I dislike what I fancy I feel.' "

If we felt no pain when we cut or burned our fingers, we might soon have no fingers. But nature has overshot its mark temporarily in the production of pain in creatures that have attained to reason. What is gained from the almost unbearable pain of a child's earache, which before the days of antibiotics, or even of lancing the eardrum, sometimes went on for days without any letup except for the small comfort produced by applications of warm oil, plus rocking in the mother's arms and being sung to a long-delayed sleep?

Since pain is recognized in the cerebral hemispheres, animals at stages too low in evolution to possess these do not feel it in the sense that we do. Humans object to pain more than any other animal, not only because we are more acutely conscious of the immediate pain, but because we remember it from the past, and dread it for the future. Furthermore we now know that something can usually be done about it, and this increases our impatience with it.

One of the greatest boons that science has given man is the discovery that certain molecules can block the signals that carry pain to the brain. Until 1920 there were only four reasonably safe anesthetic molecules in general use, but today more than a hundred are available. After a million years of intermittent physical suffering, man now has it almost entirely within his ability to accept pain when it is needed, and when it is not so needed to reduce or eliminate it with analgesics and anesthetics. Thus man gradually achieves more choice as he comes into better control of this elementary form of physical good and evil.

Higher forms of evil affect man's emotional and mental and spiritual natures through signals analogous to those sent by pain from the physical body. As we learn to recognize evil, we are able increasingly to avoid future unhappiness. One of the greatest contributions science has made to man's development is the increasing ability it gives him to see in advance the consequences of a given line of conduct. Evil is his measure of the difference between what things are and what they ought to be. As man learns to distinguish more clearly between right and wrong he does less servomechanistic "hunting," oscillating among the many kinds of happiness and suffering.

Just as from time to time people are born who have no sense of pain, an even larger number of humans are born without awareness of evil, or because of unfortunate circumstances develop no sense of moral rightness. The jails and madhouses are filled with such poor creatures, and social science is only slowly learning to take account of their unfortunate lack, dangerous to themselves and others.

In recent years there has been much discussion of the importance of "peace of mind." What is called peace of mind in this context principally involves security of spirit, which should not be confused with continuous satisfaction, comfort, rest, and freedom from all anxiety. A certain degree of anxiety is necessary for any creature having awareness, to give it an incentive force and keep it from becoming a spiritual opossum. A modicum of suffering and of the other expressions of evil are integral parts of living. Only as our understanding improves can we achieve a greater degree of control over the immediate anxiety level. Science brings both. As it makes it possible to see further into the future our anxiety may grow in proportion, but compensation is brought by the increasing equanimity of spirit that results from better understanding.

Many modern thinkers, scientists and nonscientists alike, remain pessimistic about the progress of man. Biologists especially are fond of pointing out that evolution does not necessarily result in progress, but merely in the production of something different, usually something more complex, that moves faster. But if we measure nature in the large, rather than, as some biologists do, lying under the bed and pulling the ticking apart bit by bit, we see that nature proceeds from simpler patterns to those capable of carrying out more involved processes, and there is good in the complexity that makes new accomplishments possible.

Each of us must decide for himself whether men's lives on the average are becoming richer, more satisfactory, and fuller of those things that we consider good. The more we know about science, religion, and art, the easier this is, for we are then able to use a yardstick of the proper length to measure progress, so that our conclusions will not be thrown off by the countless minor cycles that occur throughout evolution.

Science furnishes one of the best means men have discovered for discriminating between good and evil, for it increases the areas of contact between man and nature and between men and other men. Whether or not one believes that nature is impelled by motives of which humans can approve depends entirely on his own predilections. Meanwhile, let seer and scientist relax in mutual tolerance, for in the climb toward complexity and greater awareness many men have taken part, and found it good.

4

The shaking down of nature's components into new patterns capable of greater co-operative action and attainment takes much time. Man, with his newly acquired gifts of thought and imagination, is able to give a push here and a twist there to aid in the pattern formation. He needs experience to gain wisdom as the complexity of pattern increases, but he is aided in this by his curiosity, his aesthetic sense, and his essential mysticism.

As we stand in the shadow of the atomic bomb some thoughtful persons find it difficult to believe that science makes living not only more enjoyable but less dangerous. Yet we do not fear the bomb for the damage it has done but for the damage it could do. So has it been always with the new powers that have come to men, for the protection against their evil aspects, which usually comes packed in the same carton, is often not immediately visible. Man carries within himself the seeds not only of his own destruction but of his own constructiveness. These are the seeds which are good, which in the end have triumphed as more lasting, and which can be expected again to last. It is not always easy to choose in advance those aspects of things which are good, but it becomes easier as we gain experience. Science is a charted way of selecting the type of experience that pertains to cause and effect.

A question that has long interested philosophers is that of freedom of the will, as opposed to the predestination that seems inevitable if effects follow causes. To what extent can man control his own actions, and to what extent are they pre-set and built into his nature? This question has been picked to pieces until only shreds remain, but the main diffi-

culties arise from the way words are used, from the confusion between objective and subjective reality, and from
the impossible attempt to jump to the absolute instead of
appreciating the relative. If we bear in mind that we are
interested mainly in human behavior, we can reach a meaningful conclusion.

The lower a creature lies in the reaches of organic evolution, the less freedom of action does it appear to have. The
behavior of a plant or a protozoan depends largely on the
built-in responses fixed by its gene patterns. An ant or a
bee has some freedom of choice, but little compared to a man.
It may be argued that hidden attributes really control even
the apparently free choices of humans. This is almost certainly true, but such semantic shifts toward objective reality
are irrelevant, for free will is a human concept.

Each living creature is in a way like the family cow,
familiar in my boyhood, who was put out to pasture on the
side of a country lane on a rope tied to a stake. Within the
confines of her rope she was free to graze at will, though her
freedom of choice was somewhat conditioned by her built-in
predilections for clover as opposed to tumbleweed. An increase in awareness, and improved understanding of his environment on the part of any creature, results in a lengthening
of the rope. In recent years science has been making the
rope by which man is staked out much longer indeed. The
gods men long have visualized take free control over the
aspects of nature with which they are associated, and represent
the ultimate in freedom of the will.

As man awakens to greater awareness of himself and his
surroundings, he finds that he has been given the opportunity
to govern ever greater reaches of the world about him.
With this opportunity goes the responsibility that he act ever
more wisely. To be wise, he must learn ever better to pre-

dict the outcome of a given course of action, to become an increasingly good prophet.

It is the increase in responsibility that comes with increasing control over nature which makes men less like beasts and more like the gods they have always visualized. However, men can measure up to new responsibilities at only a limited rate. The regulation of this rate is today one of the outstanding problems of human relations.

As man gains in experience, and in sensitivity to new experience, he becomes increasingly able to take on and master new powers such as the release of nuclear energy. He learns increasingly that his security must come from within as well as from without. He attains greater dignity, and learns that he must accord this same dignity to all his fellows.

Man shows increasing ability to transform his knowledge into wisdom. As his competence and wisdom grow he gains control over vaster reaches of his environment, and the magnitude of his errors can grow also. But he must not falter through his fear of error, for it is thus he learns, and he can be comforted by his observation that statistically the universe is self-balancing.

We can see God's creatures being pulled slowly in the direction of their needs in accordance with their ability to fit in with the whole of nature. This basic law is embodied in the religious maxim, "Be of good courage, I have overcome the World." To implement, protect, and guide man the blessings of intelligence, imagination, and spiritual discernment have been conferred on him. These three will carry him far.

5

As we have said before, our world is today probably about halfway through its cycle of existence as a possible abode for life. The five billion years that may well remain before the sun grows cold can bring wonders of which mankind has but a faint presentiment.

Many recent books contain predictions of what is likely to happen to man as a result of science in the next decade, century, or millennium. Such extrapolation regarding specific accomplishments more than a few years away is usually unfruitful, however, except as an imagination stretcher. Short-range scientific predictions are usually found to err on the side of conservatism (except for some pseudo-scientific excursions such as the more extreme efforts in the realm of space travel). Recent predictions that airplanes would within twenty years be traveling between New York and Los Angeles in less than four hours were scarcely published before such journeys were made.

While cogitations regarding space travel are romantically appealing, we have many more important problems to occupy us for the next few decades. The moon, at 200,000 miles, offers a tempting way station to lure men into space, but the next stopping place on Mars or Venus is farther away than most people realize. Like early trans-Pacific fliers, who came to a realization that charts of the oceans are misleading because the names of islands take up so much room on a map as to give one an incorrect idea of the vast expanse of water relative to the fingerbreadths of land, we need to get a more realistic impression of the depths of space. The moon is a dry and dismal place, and one of the first realizations of any men who may arrive there will be how lucky we mortals are to have so comfortable an earth on which to dwell. It would be a foolish prophet indeed who would say that man will not become an astronaut eventually, but I will limit my predictions for the next quarter century, at least, to a few possible journeys to the moon, with the first two or three only one-way trips if landings are attempted.

We have sketched the broad picture of the new vistas opening up to man as he gains new ability to handle matter and energy. We should be much more concerned about the world's food supply than we are. No way can be seen of continuing to increase indefinitely the number of human beings able to live in the world at one time without starving. But more importantly, we should consider such things as the further development of the mind, emotions, and spirit of man, and the building of new patterns of concerted action as larger and greater groups of entities learn to co-operate.

We have seen that the human brain has doubled in size twice since man first came to reason, and that such physical changes, the result of mutations, are likely to occur unexpectedly and suddenly again. Under man's more immediate control are the development of his faculties of reason, of his understanding of and control of the emotions which govern his actions, and of those qualities of the spirit that are now at the beginning of a rapid and increasing flowering. These are the qualities that will bring men closer to perfection.

The average intelligence of humans can be expected slowly to increase, though not as measured by intelligence tests, which give only a relative indication of variations within a given culture. It is unlikely that the basic brain faculty will change much within the next few thousand years, though at any time a series of fortunate mutations might provide a new step upwards in cranial capacity and brain complexity which would ultimately spread through the entire race. Ever larger fractions of the world's population can be expected to spend increasing portions of their time on formal and informal education. Even more important in the immediate future will be increased attainment on the level of co-operative social effort.

The increasing leisure that will result from better harnessing of energy and matter most assuredly will not result in increased boredom. While there will always be people who are naturally lazy and bored, the survival values and self-rectifying features of the human spirit prevent this from becoming general, and men, ever more curious, ever more aesthetically stimulated, can be expected to become continually more interested in the outer world as well as the inner worlds of the mind and spirit. Personal selfishness, a built-in virtue on any new level of development which becomes a vice when higher levels are achieved, will, as we measure it today, decline, and the center of gravity of man's troubles and anxieties will gradually move from the physical toward more subtle, spiritual, or more broadly inclusive levels.

In a million years man has surpassed the ape in ways far more important, even from what might be called a godlike viewpoint, than those in which the ape surpassed the amoeba in something approaching a billion years. What then can nature not do in the next million years, to say nothing of the five thousand million that may be available? Our ultrahuman successors are likely to see far more progress than evolution has yet brought forth, for the development of higher forms of life proceeds in geometrical rather than arithmetical fashion. Instead of merely growing longer like blades of grass, the parts of nature proliferate like a branching tree, so that each of ten new limbs may bring forth as many new twigs. If life on earth is today a trillion times as complex as it was a billion years ago, it can well become a trillion times more complex, ordered, and meaningful at an equal time in the future. And we err if we consider this complexity as confusing or forbidding, for it will not be just a multiplication of what we now know, but full of new things as foreign to our present ken as creative imagination is foreign to a sponge.

Thus far, nucleons on earth have been able to swing into the patterns that form atoms, the atoms into molecules, the molecules into crystals and cells, the cells into plant and animal creatures. In many of these creatures sensation and emotion and reason and imagination and spiritual aspiration have begun to develop. Societies of ever higher types, from termite and ant colonies to the United Nations, are formed. What further patterns may not arise, what new expressions of the verities which we call eternal but which are only potential when atoms move only in the disorder of a world as yet unformed?

The picture of the expanding evolution of our universe, inanimate into animate, these into ever higher living forms, as atoms gather into stars and plants and men, is far more stimulating than the relatively static pictures seen by our forefathers, imperfect and greatly distorted snapshots of the truth. The views we hold today are imperfect also, but as we see farther into nature and gather improved sets of illusions we can demonstrate greater success as prophets, and thus show that we depart from reality to an ever smaller degree.

We see a vast universe unfolding from simplicity into complexity as its components interact, developing new patterns in which the useful is preserved in accordance with its contribution. Matter appears, under the proper influence of energy, to obey inherent urges to achieve ever greater complexity of form and pattern, of which those parts that lead to more successful living are differentially preserved. Call this blind evolution, or the breath of life, or the hand of God, as you will, the over-all result, the building up of creatures increasingly like gods can well move us to great reverence. Humans long innately for perfection, for increasing awareness, and for the ability to control increasing reaches of their environment. Man can rejoice to find about him so beneficent a setting for fulfilling these aspirations.

We must grow with our universe! It is turning out to be much more marvelous than man has ever dreamed, more beautiful while more complex, fuller of that which we consider good than philosophers of earlier days could dare to expect. Man's new directions of thought are filled with meaning for the coming races of mankind, and will lead him into new fields of awareness, new challenges of attainment, and new realizations of human destiny.

There is still far more in heaven and earth than is dreamt of in all our philosophies, but man is climbing and nature loses nothing of its wonder as he climbs. Beyond the human state stretch apparently unlimited opportunities for further evolution. Man has seen the gods, the essences of perfection, and knows within his heart that by following his inner light, learning how to control himself and the ever-increasing reaches of his universe, he can become like them.

New knowledge brings challenge, change, and opportunity. Man is periodically forced further to renounce his tendency to isolationism and self-sufficiency, to seek mutual understanding and co-operation with his fellows. Science, as an integral part of man's own being, helps him to rise to this great challenge.

Afterword

I hope that readers interested in backgrounds will be slow to label the points of view presented in this book as being those of any specific group or groups. I remember especially in this connection the comments of a critic of my earlier book, "Atoms in Action," who, because I emphasized the importance of energy control in human affairs, quite mistakenly labeled my point of view as that of a technocrat. All too often a single glimpse of truth leads to an ism, a straight line drawn tangent to the curve of truth at a point of revelation. In attempting to present an integrated, though necessarily limited, glimpse of man's scientific view of himself, which would be meaningful to modern citizens having various degrees of previous polarization towards science, I have tried to balance evidence from many relevant points of view.

In attempting to keep the discussion on as impersonal a level as possible, and in the interest of conciseness, I have deliberately omitted most of the labels designating the authors of particular discoveries or theories. A blanket apology therefore goes to all whose brain children have been taken from the pile of human knowledge without specific credit or reference.

It would be surprising if a number of inaccuracies had not crept into a discussion covering so many fields of science. In any case the number of misstatements that remain has been greatly reduced through the kindness of scientific colleagues and friends who have most affably criticized chapters dealing with fields in which they were far more expert than I. I am especially indebted in this regard to Drs. Irwin W. Sizer and Francis O. Schmitt of the Department of Biology at M.I.T.; to Dr. George Wald of the corresponding department at Harvard; to Dr. Harlow Shapley of the Harvard Observatory; to Drs. Arthur C. Cope, John C. Sheehan, and Frederick D. Greene of the Department of Chemistry at M.I.T.; to Dr. James H. Means and Dr. Dana L. Farnsworth of the Medical Departments of M.I.T. and Harvard respectively; to Professor Robert R. Shrock of the Department of Geology and Geophysics at M.I.T.; and to Professor Samuel A. Goldblith of the M.I.T. Department of Food Technology. Many other colleagues have aided me by answering specific queries lying in their specialties. Despite the kindly discipline of all these referees some slips doubtless remain, and these are my responsibility. It is my belief that they are not such as to discredit the basic arguments.

G. R. H.

Cambridge, Massachusetts
April 16, 1956

Index